Lou

SO-ASB-746

In this
LAND
of
EVE

In this
LAND
of
EVE

J. Birney Dibble

ABINGDON PRESS   New York • Nashville

Winona Lake
Free Methodist Church
Library

IN THIS LAND OF EVE

Copyright © 1965 by Abingdon Press

All rights in this book are reserved.
No part of the book may be reproduced in any manner whatsoever without written permission of the
publishers except brief quotations embodied in criti-
cal articles or reviews. For information address
Abingdon Press, Nashville, Tennessee.

Library of Congress Catalog Card Number: 65-20367

SET UP, PRINTED, AND BOUND BY THE
PARTHENON PRESS, AT NASHVILLE,
TENNESSEE, UNITED STATES OF AMERICA

To:

Mr. Sampson Paulo, who was born in the African Bush, who died there in the springtime of his life, and who demonstrated with his life how well the African can be trained in the sciences

To:

Dr. Joseph Norquist, doctor-in-charge of the Kiomboi Lutheran Hospital, whose medical skills in many fields and whose diplomacy in many crises have maintained the reputation which that hospital has in East Africa

FOREWORD

It is fascinating to observe firsthand the truth of the saying that no man is an island. The lives of all of us are in-
extricably intertwined, influenced on the one hand, in-
fluencing on the other. Take Bob Jensen and Marc
Gravdahl and myself—all of us as different from the
other as a Masai warrior from an Amazon or an American
suburbanite. But all of us interacting with the others so
that I heard of the plight of the Kiomboi Hospital in
Tanganyika through Dr. Jensen, who was invited to Eau
Claire by Pastor Gravdahl. The contrast between the
medical situation in Tanganyika and in Eau Claire was
almost unbelievable. At Kiomboi, Tanganyika: one doctor
for 600,000 people. At Eau Claire: fifty doctors for 75,000
people.

I couldn't get this out of my mind, and I turned it over
and over as I drove slowly home. I sent up a trial balloon,
not really knowing what to expect from my wife. "How
would you like to go to Africa for a year?" She knew the
nature of the meeting I had attended, and with hardly
a pause, said, "Oh, I'd love to. When do we go?"

That settled it, as far as we were concerned, and within a year we had passed the strict examinations of the Augustana Lutheran Board of World Missions (despite the disadvantage of being Methodists), and were sent to Kiomboi Lutheran Hospital, Tanganyika, in July, 1962.

This is the story of that year.

CONTENTS

INTRODUCTION 11

1. THE MOTIVATION 15

2. THE KIOMBOI MISSION STATION 19

3. THE HOSPITAL—MONDAY 25

4. IRAMBA-LAND 45

5. THE HOSPITAL—TUESDAY 53

6. THE BUSH 69

7. THE HUNT—WEDNESDAY 80

8. CHICKEN LIVERS, DICED PLACENTAE,
   AND CASTOR BEANS 89

9. THE DOCTOR LAUGHED 99

10. THE HOSPITAL—THURSDAY 106

11. THE HOSPITAL—FRIDAY 112

12. THE SINGING SPEARS IN
        THE VALLEY OF THE BARABAIG........118

13. THE SPIRIT OF THE DONKEY 129

14. EASTER SUNDAY 140

15. THE WAKINDIGA 146

EPILOGUE 158

INTRODUCTION

It is October, 1963. The rainy season has not yet begun. The evening sun burns hot and dry over the hospital compound, but in the east the sky blackens as if to rain. And about the time the rains come—in a month or two—I must leave this desk, and this house, and this land, and face the cultural shock of America. Before I leave, I must capture for myself, and for others who care to join with me, the barest hint of what I have experienced here on this plateau in central Tanganyika. Here, where a century ago Livingstone lived out his life, and where his heart is still buried. Here, where a hopeful people named their capital city The Port of Peace.* Here, where missionaries have introduced a two-edged sword, one edge cutting through ignorance with education, disease with medicine, heathenism with the gospel, and the other edge cutting through the lid on Pandora's box to release the still-to-be-controlled furies of nationalism.

Now a full range of kaleidoscopic pictures flood my mind as I look back on the last year and a half: the fare-well tears not yet dry when the stewardess announced that we must fasten our seat belts for the landing at La

* The city of Dar es Salaam, capital of the Republic of Tanganyika.

11

Guardia, one hour out of Chicago; the pell-mell rush through England, Denmark, Italy; the furnace heat of Khartoum; the ugly brown dryness of Kenya from the air; the banana-selling boys in Arusha; dik-diks (terrier-sized antelopes) scattering in front of the Land-Rover during the nighttime drive to Singida; the final arrival at Kiomboi one year and many dreams since Bob Jensen's visit to Eau Claire; the work, the fun, the inspirations, the frustrations, the gratifications, the disappointments, the laughter, and the tears of a year in the bush and farm-lands of Iramba-land, deep in the heart of this old, old country, now new to the councils of independent nations. We can hear the ringing song of freedom, "Nchi Yangu" (My Country), as the Tanganyikan version of the spirit of '76 raises hopes of fulfilling dreams as yet undreamed by the masses. Dreams like that of Dr. Bob Jensen—a medical school in the cornfield which stretches from our perch on a ten-foot anthill to the slopes of Kilimanjaro. Or the dream of Pastor Bob Ward—a cross-topped church in the valley stretching from the Masai steppes to the Kindira Mountains, home of the primitive, nomadic Wakindiga. Or the dreams of Dr. Joe Norquist and myself which we have sitting in the doctors' office at Kiomboi—a new hospital with a good X-ray machine, a new laboratory, and, more important, a renewed spirit of love and cooperation.

The sun now sets on the British Empire. India has a generation of young people who never knew the British, and one by one Britain's other colonies are following in India's footsteps. On December 7, 1962, Tanganyika buried the flag it had pulled down a year before, and planted the gold, green, and black symbol of the new nation atop Africa's highest mountain. If you will stand as I did, halfway up Mt. Kilimanjaro, you will recognize the strength of that symbolic raising of the flag. Watch the storm-clouds roll on the twin peaks, with the equatorial sun beating on your head, and between the clouds a rainbow forms and evanesces and forms again— Kibo all covered with snow, and Mawenzi all slanted black rock and roiling mists and rain. Kibo is the hope, and Mawenzi the strength. The hope is high, almost unobtainable, but distant goals have been reached before, and isn't that flag still there?

Much of what you see and hear in Tanganyika is nowadays influenced by the fact that freedom from British rule has come. Not that you can notice any difference down in the bush, nor are the roads much better, nor is education yet universal. Nor does the government run more efficiently; on the contrary, the processes of government grind on erratically with gross inefficiency, especially in the small villages where once highly trained Britishers handling the affairs of the communities have been replaced in many instances by political appointees whose knowledge of government is being learned "on the job." But untrained as they are, they are bustling, eager men, and what they lack in experience you must hope they will make up in desire to push their people forward.

So, although this report is not to be a treatise on the politics of Tanganyika, it will be colored by political overtones and undercurrents. With these background thoughts in mind, let us now set out on the adventure which I have called . . . "In this land of Eve."

For we were

    adrift on seas of bush and thorn
       in this land of Eve where man was born.
    Or at least we're told that here men bred
       from a race of pre-men long since dead,
    For out on this long green-yellow plain
       is the spot where Abel was slain by Cain.

1

THE MOTIVATION

We sat groggily slumped in the narrow seats of the night-flight to Khartoum. Rome was a memory of crumbling ruins, cedars on the Appian Way, garbage in the streets, and cats in the parks. Nine hours before, we had watched night black out the Mediterranean while we soared in sunlight at 27,000 feet. Now at four in the morning the high-pitched whine of the jets changed to a rumbling, grumbling roar as the plane began settling down for the landing at Khartoum in the Sudan, where the Blue Nile joins the White Nile, and where General Charles G. Gordon was murdered on the steps of his palace. This was our first stop in Africa, and thrills of excitement tingled in our blood as we accepted the blast of hot humid air that greeted us in the predawn darkness. We knew that it was right here in Khartoum that Gordon sought to wrest the Sudan from the religious Muslim fanaticism of the Madhi, to restore peace and order to the Sudan, and to rid the area of the despicable slave trade that was to eventually reduce the population of the territory of Uganda to twenty-five percent of its original number.

In the modern airport waiting room in this history-suffused town on the Nile, we sipped cold Coca-Cola and passed the time with an Indian merchant en route from

15

Europe to his home in the Seychelles, while red-fezzed waiters hovered at our elbows. Then on to Kenya, to the largest airport in Africa at Nairobi, where we waited, tired and impatient, for four hours, while our battered old DC-3 of the East African Airways was repaired for the flight to Arusha. And finally our first sight of Tanganyika, at about one thousand feet, with Barbara and Edna and me sick from the air pockets, and Eric happily munching away at the best parts of our four box lunches.

At Arusha, Dr. Joe Norquist met us in the Kiomboi Station Land Rover TD 673, with big smiles all around.

> Joe: It's hard to believe you're really here!
> Birney: Yeah, it's kind of hard for us to believe, too. Now how do we get out of the airport—customs and all that?
> Joe: No problem. Your luggage off the plane yet?

And so forth. Small talk to hide the deeper meanings of this meeting.

People had asked us, "How can you think of going to Africa, especially with your children? Aren't you afraid of the animals, the snakes, the people? Why, look what happened in Kenya, and look what's going on in South Africa, and in the Congo. Aren't you afraid?" One finds it difficult to answer this kind of a question face to face without sounding pompous, or holier-than-thou, or flippant, but I am going to answer it now, to lay it to rest forever.

Ernest Gann, in prefacing his book *Fate is the Hunter*, quotes Taikung Jen in an explanation of how to escape death. The method is never to get out in front to lead, nor ever to lag too far behind. "A tree with a straight trunk is the first to be chopped down. A well with sweet water is the first to be drawn dry."

This is the way to escape death. Never push yourself

16

into the lead, never accept challenges, never go on to higher education, never do anything which might lead to a position of importance or danger. I say, is this escaping death, or is it escaping life?

When I was very small, my mother chanced one day to look out the window and saw me hanging by my knees from a branch of the big pear tree. Her first impulse was to rush out and tell me to get right down, but my father cautioned her to let me be—to show her fear would only make me afraid, and then I would be sure to fall. Psychiatrists know that fear of falling (or failing) can wreak more havoc in a person's life than a fall itself.

If one is to spend his life escaping physical death, he soon finds he is hedging himself into a tighter and tighter enclosure. Physical death is nothing to be laughed at, nothing to ignore; only a psychotic person can laugh at death. But it is also not something to be feared to the exclusion of accepting new challenges.

People also said, "How can you give up a year's income, give up a year of your life, for such a venture." This is a good time to take *that* shade by the heels and lay it to rest. This last year has not been *taken* from my life; it has been *added* to my life. The lives of my family and myself have been immeasurably enriched by this year, some evidences of which may become clearer in the content of this report.

Others, more sympathetic with the purpose of our mission, and meaning well, said, "God bless you. You are making sacrifices that few will make." Looking back, I rather think we accepted this kind of tribute with too little attempt at refutation. But if there was any of this unwarranted pride, it disappeared quickly, as humbleness rolled in like the tides from the sea. Meet Margaret Peterson, in Africa since 1939, and try not to be humble. Meet Dr. Olson, in China, India, and now Africa for a lifetime of over forty years, and try not to be humble. And meet Hal and Louise Faust, and Bob and Jean Ward, and Alice Turnbladh, and—oh, meet the whole "family" of Iramba-land missionaries who have been here two, or three, or four terms of four years each—and try not to be humble. Although we certainly hope that our contribution has been worthwhile, it is of Lilliputian size in a Gulliver world. Truly, the harvest is great, and the helpers few.

2

THE KIOMBOI MISSION STATION

On leaving Singida, heading northwest sixty miles to
Kiomboi, a traveler does indeed feel "adrift on seas of
bush and thorn." Climbing the south end of the escarpment at Iguguno, he can look back, and can see, as far
as the golden haze will allow, rolling hills of thorn trees
and thornbushes here and there broken by small farms.
The incomprehensible immensity of Africa is nowhere
better seen than from the Iramba plateau. Space and
trees and bush and farm, hill and river, mountains high—
for there's Mt. Hanang across the valley in Barabaig-land,
twelve thousand feet above the sea. And if the traveler
takes the trouble to climb the tumbling rocks to the old
German fort halfway between Kiomboi and Kinampanda
on the west escarpment he will be rewarded on a clear
day with a view of the rim of the Ngorongoro Crater
one hundred and twenty air miles away!

Once the lower edge of the escarpment is climbed and
the plateau reached, the road progressively climbs another several hundred feet during the next forty miles.
It is all up and down over these rolling hills, but it is
more up than down. For the most part, the countryside
is scattered with small farms, and the road passes several
small villages. There are long stretches of completely

unpopulated wilderness however, and we have seen, on many occasions, lion, leopard, giraffe, wild boar, impala, dik-dik, snakes, and other denizens of the bush.

There are always an amazing number of people, too, along the road, going from town to town, or farm to farm, or merely out for a stroll. And many ask the traveler for a ride. (We usually have a full load of supplies and people, and since buses run at known times and for a few shillings, we do not feel obligated to serve as a free taxi service, especially when our vehicle insurance policies specifically exclude the casual rider from liability coverage. Even along rather lonely stretches, we are always amazed to see the number of people that materialize seemingly from nowhere if we have car trouble, ready to help or just to watch.)

The first sign of foreign intrusion comes fifty miles from Singida, where the traveler comes upon a small Catholic church and parish house perched upon a hill above the Kironda River. Then, as he continues on, the road drops down into the valley of the Kironda, and there is an old-looking gold mine, operated first by the Germans before World War I, and now owned by Mr. and Mrs. Bichieri, a wonderful couple, and their daughter and son-in-law, Mimi and Don Mustard. Don, originally from Scotland, is a well-trained geologist and is making plans to reopen the mine if it can be done profitably under the new socialist government.

Then, after proceeding up the other side of the valley, through the heart of Iramba-land, with millet fields on both sides extending to the horizon, and into the little village of Kiomboi, the traveler has reached his destination. A sign points straight ahead to the "Mission Hospital," and to the right to "Boma," which is the political nerve center of Kiomboi-land. A quarter of a mile further through corn and millet fields and a cluster of Iramba houses, and there is the hospital compound.

The visitor's first reaction to the compound is usually a pleasant one. The main road, sand and gravel, passes the big square water tank, then goes past roads to right and left which lead to the missionaries' houses. The road then goes past long brick dormitories for the student nurses, then the primary school (enrollment about a hundred African children, grades 1-4) and finally reaches the main hospital itself. The hospital is composed of five main wards, laboratory, classrooms, storerooms, and the main administration building which also houses admitting rooms, main operating rooms, and drugroom. All these various buildings are of one story and are connected to each other by a U-shaped ramp of concrete, covered for protection against sun and rain. A beautiful little chapel sits off a little to the side. The outpatient building is also separate.

Continuing the tour now on foot, the visitor turns up a road parallel to the main road, and here passes the small well-built houses of the African staff of nurses, medical assistants, nurses' aids, and other ancillary personnel such as the hospital chaplain and hospital maintenance men. Further up are the rather dilapidated houses of the primary school teachers. The visitor walks through a half acre of corn and peanuts and comes to one of the houses usually occupied by a missionary doctor which has been occupied during the past year by the Dibbles. It is a stone bungalow, thirty years old, with a large screened-in back porch. The roof is of corrugated aluminum, and all the windows are covered with both ordinary screening and a metal latticework resembling cyclone fencing. Inside, the rooms are large, cool, and floored with solid concrete. The front door opens onto a long room which serves as entryway, living room, and dining room. In the entryway sits a beat-up old green sofa, partly reclaimed to usefulness by a green throw. It is utilized mostly by the children in play or as a fold-out bed when there is company, or by the dog Jet and his frequent canine visitor from the Norquists. In the living room part of the room there is a more modern sofa, built in Singida by Kapoor Singh. Two easy chairs occupy two corners, and a coffee table in front of the sofa and two end tables at either end complete the furniture. In the dining room are a table and chairs and a buffet for storing dishes, silverware, and table linens. Three of the bedrooms open off the main room, and in addition, the kitchen, bathroom, and the back porch open off the main room. The kitchen has a wooden sink with aluminum basins, a kerosene refrigerator (over which I might have cursed many a time if I had not been a missionary!), a stove fed by a large tank of bottled gas standing alongside, a large worktable covered with metal sheeting, an upright screened cupboard for foodstuffs, and a huge eight-foot-high cupboard for kitchen ware, canned goods, and so forth. Opening off the back porch are two more rooms, one of which is used for storage and as a workroom, and the other as a study and for the shortwave radio. In all, a rather comfortable, livable house. The visitor will notice, as we have often said, that we don't have furniture of either French Provincial, or Danish Modern, but rather Early Mission!

Continuing on down the road, the visitor passes three more houses, each a little different but basically similar in construction and inside format, in which live the other missionaries connected with the hospital. In the first, three nurses; in the second, two nurses and a laboratory technician; and in the third, Dr. Norquist and his family. Farther down the road there is the Augustana School, a boarding school for the children of missionaries all over Tanganyika, with a varying enrollment of sixty-five to ninety children in the first eight grades. Here there are three more houses, newly constructed, for the "house parents" and teachers. Here also are the workshops and storerooms which serve the entire compound, schools, hospital, and houses, under the direction of Fred Malloy who also doubles as the male half of the house-parents. Fred is the number one big-game hunter at the Kiomboi Mission.

A stone's throw from the Augustana School is the African church, now in the process of receiving badly needed repairs. The inside has been completely replastered and painted a light blue, and a new bas-relief cross beautifies the wall above the small altar. The church is large, the main room being about one hundred by thirty feet in dimensions. The floor is concrete, and the seats are low backless benches occupying about two thirds of the room. The church, started and for many years served by a missionary pastor, now has an African pastor and an assistant pastor, also African. Two services are held each Sunday, the first in the local dialect, Kinylamba, and the second in Swahili. Many of the women and some of the men and children do not know Swahili, so the first service is very necessary. It recalls to mind the many churches in the United States that required services in German, Swedish, Polish, and so forth, for many years.

This completes the tour of the physical property. The entire compound occupies an area which would cover about half a section of farmland in the United States, that is, about one-half mile on a side. Except for small plots of grass around the missionaries' houses and around the hospital and schools, the compound is no different from the surrounding countryside—thornbush, tall grass, scattered trees (baobab, eucalyptus, mango, acacia, and assorted others unidentified), criss-crossing footpaths, and several roads. Most of the African staff and several of the missionaries have gardens of papaya, corn, squash, peanuts, carrots, and potatoes, so the whole effect is that of living on a farm, especially with the cacophony of roosters at 6:30 each morning. Donkeys and cows frequently wander through the yards, despite our efforts to keep them out. Hyenas prowl at night, and both lions and leopards have been seen on the compound. Snakes abound. But let us leave this description of the buildings and look at the reason for all this—the hospital and its work.

3

THE HOSPITAL—MONDAY

As he passed by, he saw a man blind from his birth. And his disciples asked him, "Rabbi, who sinned, this man or his parents, that he was born blind?" Jesus answered, "It was not that this man sinned, or his parents, but that the works of God might be made manifest in him. We must work the works of him who sent me, while it is day; night comes, when no one can work"—John 9:1-4.

This passage may explain the position of the hospital in the overall structure of the evangelical work of the church. It certainly goes much further, to my mind at least, than the admonition to go and heal so that men might have health. It takes that one important further step past this admonition to preach, teach, and heal, because it considers the point of healing that of making the works of God manifest. One must be careful here. It should not be assumed by the casual thinker that this means that one can ignore the simple act of healing and the effect that this has on the life of the person who has been healed. The simple act of healing is of great importance—both to the healed and to the healer. To be able to heal a person is a God-given ability, but healing occurs daily in the hands of men who give not a thought to the spiritual significance of the act and who are not interested one whit in making the works of God manifest.

25

And who is to say that they are not doing a good work? Certainly not I. And certainly not their patients, who are benefited by being returned whole to family, work, and community.

But on the mission field, one must take that one further step—to heal the sick *not only* to make them well, *but also* to make the works of God manifest. It is this witness of God's nature and this witness to the gospel of Jesus Christ that *fulfills* the mission of the hospital. Let no one argue that it is not good merely to place the healing profession in the midst of a people that has not produced its own healers; this is good, in itself. And it is being done with gratifying results, by private and governmental agencies of many nations including—and especially—our own. But also let no man say that that should be the only purpose of the Christian hospital in the same situation. Heal to make men whole? Yes! But also heal that the works of God may be made manifest!

But a man cannot talk forever in platitudes, however pious, and he must eventually get down to work. And this is what I did, and this is what I propose to discuss in the next part of this report. To do this, I have chosen the vehicle of the diary, dull as it may sometimes seem. But then life is sometimes dull, and honest reporting should not glamorize where events are not glamorous. I shall describe the events of one week, as I lived it, a day at a time, and to break up the narration's monotony, I shall intersperse between these personal notes other chapters of a more general nature, in order that the reader may more readily identify with the modern medical missionary and the people he serves.

MONDAY

6:55 AM: The alarm goes off, hidden in the clothes closet, since Edna cannot stand to hear the old wind-up clanking away all night. Edna rolls out, with scarcely a glance at the bright red sun climbing the palmetto trees outside our window, and heads for the kitchen to start breakfast. I roll out the other side, fumbling with the mosquito netting, and head for the back study to operate the shortwave radio.

7:00: "A.L.M. One, Queen Roger Uncle. Two. Three (very loud). Five. Five. Alpha, wake up!" It is Doug Augustine, at Kinampanda, calling the roll of the twelve Augustana Lutheran Mission stations where we still have missionaries. My call number is seven, and since eight (Wembere) is below the escarpment and can't hear any-one but me, I relay to them (Queen Sugar Oboe). For ten or fifteen minutes, messages are exchanged on our private network. Some are important, some even urgent, many merely for convenience. Being the only doctor on the net, I serve as medical adviser to the dispensaries, and frequently discuss a case with a nurse, proscribe procedure, and prescribe treatment. On occasion, the advice can only be "Send the patient in," and a way must be found to get the patient here to Kiomboi from as far away as Barabaig-land, which is over a hundred miles away, or about four hours. This morning, however, there are only routine messages, and by 7:10 I hear, "Seven, you may Tare." To which I reply, "Able Roger, Seven."

7:15: Edna has a pan of hot water for my morning shave. I pick it up out in the kitchen and proceed with my ablutions, with Gillette superblues from England, Ingram lather from Middlesex, and Colgate toothpaste from the U.S.A.

7:30: Breakfast. Rice Krispies, that go Klap, Knetter, Kraak instead of Snap, Crackle, Pop since they are from South Africa (despite the boycott), and do they ever smaakliker met Koue melk! And if you care to make koekies, why just remember Karamelkoekies ist so heerlik enso maklik om te maak!

7:55: I leave the house, walk down through the corn, bean, and peanut fields, past the African staff houses, to the chapel. The bell is ringing in the wards, and the staff and student nurses come up from the hospital for morning vespers. This service lasts from fifteen to twenty minutes and is led by a different person each morning. I took my turn just a week ago, using as my text the story of Jesus as a boy in the temple with the elders. The services are in Swahili.

8:25: I meet Mr. Godson Mangare on the ramp by the nursing school office, and we start out on rounds, working backwards this morning from Ward E to Ward A. Mr. Mangare is a Medical Assistant. His training consisted of a three-year course at Bumbuli, in the Usambara Mountains near Moshi, following a preparation approximately equivalent to our junior college graduates in the United States. His knowledge of tropical medicine far exceeds mine, and when Joe Norquist is gone, I rely heavily on Mr. Mangare (rhymes with starry). His training in surgery, obstetrics, and fractures was necessarily limited, but he has a keen mind and has amassed a rather impressive knowledge in these fields also. His special interests lie in the laboratory, and if he were given the opportunity, he would probably make an excellent pathologist. It is alternately encouraging to see what these MA's can do and discouraging at times to spot great hiatuses in their knowledge.

8:30: On Ward E (Gynecology) we are accompanied by staff nurse Mrs. Elisifa Shani who graduated from Kiomboi Nurses Training Centre and met and married Mr. Hezekiah Shani here. Mr. Shani is an MA, and has been in the United States in pre-med at Gustavus Adolphus College for the past year. We start around the ward.

The first patient has had a threatened miscarriage, but seems to be quieting down on bed rest and stilbesterol, a hormone drug. The second was admitted yesterday with a huge abdominal tumor, seemingly arising from the pelvis; she is scheduled for surgery tomorrow. The third patient is postoperative three days, having had a large hole between the bladder and vagina repaired; she had delivered at home nine months before and had leaked urine steadily without control during this period before seeking help. The fourth patient is six months pregnant, with a belly full of fluid, wasting of the entire body, cracking of the corners of the mouth, a bright red tongue, and a huge spleen; diagnosis: extreme protein and vitamin deficiency, and possibly cirrhosis of the liver. The fifth patient was explored for a right-sided tender cystic mass, and everybody agreed that it couldn't be an appendiceal abscess since no one present had ever seen appendicitis in an African; so of course it turned out to be an appendiceal abscess! (Note to MD's: no McBurney incision here!) The sixth patient was delivered at home by a native midwife and had had a retained placenta. The placenta was manually extracted with bare hands, and the patient developed a severe childbed fever. An abscess may be developing outside of the uterus, due to a perforation, and it may have to be drained surgically.

9:05: And so on around the ward. There are thirteen patients in gynecology today. We move on to Ward D, obstetrics. Here we are accompanied by staff nurse Mrs. Martha Mangare, married to Mr. Mangare just a few weeks ago. She directs us to those patients she thinks we should see. She is a registered midwife. Here everyone is in good condition, including two postoperative Cesarean sections. One of the sections had been done as a repeat; the other had been in labor for five days at home and we sectioned her with the baby's heart beating fit-

29

fully and with the baby's stool staining the bag of waters (indicating a dying baby); both babies are fine. There are seventeen patients on obstetrics this morning. Of these, fourteen have been delivered by the midwives. The midwives are under our general supervision, and are under the direct supervision of Greta Engborg, who was trained in nursing in New York and in midwifery at Edinburgh, Scotland. Even after a year I am not accustomed to this practice, nor resigned to it, but it is true that the doctor is called frequently and early to see patients in which there exists the slightest deviation from the normal course of labor. When in Rome. . . .

9:15: Mr. Mangare and I pass down the ramp from Ward D to Ward C. The patients' relatives are congregated in the open courtyard behind Ward C cleaning up their cooking pans and watergourds and wooden spoons. They have cooked breakfast for their sick relatives over open fires, in the bright cold sunlight, and after having fed the sick ones, have now been shooed outside so that the doctors can make rounds unharried by anxious relatives. Ward C is a decrepit old building compared to our other four wards, and it is scheduled for demolition the very minute funds are available for reconstruction. It is dark, very difficult to keep clean because of the nature of the construction, and impossible to keep free of flies and mosquitoes. It always smells of kerosene, boiling water, fly spray, and assorted other odors.

On C we are joined by staff nurses Mr. Gideon Jumbe and Mr. David Msengi. Mr. Jumbe is a veteran of almost ten years; Mr. Msengi, a neophyte from the last graduating class. The first patient, a five-year-old boy, has meningitis, probably viral, because of the near-total lack of response to antibiotics, but he is slowly recovering. The second patient, an elderly woman, has a flaming red eye with a deep laceration across the cornea, all the internal fluids having escaped—an injury caused by her husband. The third patient is a seven-year-old boy with bilharzia (snail fever), with bloody urine. The fourth is a forty-year-old woman with what we in our ignorance have called Banti's syndrome, realizing full well that we have stopped short. The fifth is a case of heart failure, responding to standard regimen. The sixth is a young man with a burn of the leg, whom I brought back from Iambi recently when over there for a dispensary visit; he is being prepared for skin grafting. The seventh patient is a relapsing fever case; the eighth, malaria and pneumonia in a one-year-old. (When infants are admitted, the mother is admitted also, given hospital clothes, and sleeps with the infant. In virtually every case the children nurse until age two to three, so it would be impractical to do otherwise. Also, the mother is far more capable and efficient in caring for the infant, especially here where the staff is small.) The ninth patient, a five-year-old boy, had the left side of his face torn off by a hyena; the left upper lip, three fourths of the nose, the eyebrow, and the skin of the entire left face were torn off. The eye is still in place, but blinded, and will have to be removed surgically. We have nearly finished grafting the wound, and in coming weeks hope to be able to reconstruct the lip, and possibly even make some kind of a nose. I haven't had much experience in the latter, but I should at least be able to improve things.* The tenth patient is a week-old twin, with malaria and pneumonia. The eleventh is a patient three years old with malaria and relapsing fever. And so on around the ward, some cases interesting medically, some more routine.

* Shortly after this was written, the father took the child out of the hospital, and, realizing that he belonged to a tribe which would never accept the child back into its midst deformed, put him out in the bush, where he was presumably killed and eaten by hyenas or other wild animals. See "The Spirit of the Donkey," Chap. 13.

9:40: We move along now to Ward B. I shall not discuss each case, though the ward is full as usual. Staff nurse Mr. Yarno Lukumo helps us here. He has recently been transferred from the Iambi Leprosarium where he worked with lepers for six years. This ward is for women and children exclusively. In the second bed is a severely dehydrated infant with a nonspecific diarrhea. She is being treated with kaolin, UNICEF milk supplementing mother's milk, and fluids given beneath the skin. In bed eight is a ten-year-old girl whose leg we amputated ten days ago because of gangrene following a puff adder bite. She is now nearly healed and is up on crutches. In bed ten is a young woman whose right arm we amputated two days ago, on Saturday morning, for gangrene following a neglected burn. She is extremely toxic still, but improving. In bed thirteen is a teacher's infant with severe cerebral malaria. She has been convulsing every ten to fifteen minutes for several days. We have given her as much chloroquin as we dare and have reluctantly almost given up hope; the mother is still hopeful and we are encouraged.

In bed fourteen is an elderly woman who had a mammoth abdominal tumor which we thought was likely spleen, but because of its shape and size we weren't sure. It was extremely tender, and she agreed to surgery. It turned out to be a spleen of 3500 grams (more than twice the size of the normal liver, and twenty times the size of the normal spleen), and was the seat of multiple infarcts (dead areas of tissue caused by blood clots), which explained the tenderness. Sections were sent to the pathology lab at Princess Margaret Hospital in Dar es Salaam to see if some other disease might be present. She is now six days postop and very happy without the heavy load and severe pain with which she had lived for months. In bed sixteen is a pitiful little lady with an epigastric (upper abdominal) mass which, on exploration, was found to be an inoperable cancer of the stomach.

In bed seventeen is a fifty-year-old woman for whom we did a radical breast removal for cancer of the left breast. She is very anemic and convalescing very slowly. In bed nineteen is a patient with an intertrochanteric fracture of the femur (hip fracture), whom we have elected to treat in traction because of the extreme shattering. We have obtained adequate length and the leg should be near perfect, functionally, in a few months. In bed twenty is a forty-five-year-old woman with a fracture of the lower third of the femur, for whom we introduced a Küntscher nail three weeks ago for internal fixation. She has a good range of motion except for incomplete extension.

10:15: We go on to Ward A, passing the two private rooms in the corridor. In one is a twenty-year-old young man who is a mental patient, and who appears to me to be schizophrenic. We are trying to make arrangements to send him to Dodoma Mental Hospital, two hundred miles away to the south of us. He will have to be taken at public expense, possibly by the police. In the other private room is a year-old infant with tetanus. We have blankets hung at the window and "Quiet" signs in Swahili and the Kinylamba dialect hung on the door. The baby is improving slowly. She has never been extremely ill, and we never did a tracheostomy. We see so many cases of lockjaw and practically all of them get well, so we have a considerably more relaxed attitude toward the condition than we have at home. I have done a tracheostomy in only one case here, and that patient proceeded to die anyway.

10:30: On Ward A, we are escorted by staff nurse Mr. Marko Shila and Mr. Jumbe. Mr. Shila is also a graduate of KNTC, and in addition has recently completed an

33

upgrading course in Dar es Salaam which is designed to graduate students with a Grade A classification, whereas our own graduates are classified Grade B. We start picking up speed now, and rapidly see patients with malaria, bowel inflammation, testicle inflammation, carbuncle of the neck, snail fever, blindness due to scarring of the cornea, abscesses of great muscles. Also, I stop a little longer with a patient scheduled for prostatectomy later in the week, and with another on whom I did a large direct hernia repair three days ago.

11: 00: We have seen almost a hundred patients in two and a half hours; our total bed capacity is a hundred and twelve. We have scheduled five patients for surgery tomorrow. Mr. Mangare and I separate now, he to work on the wards admitting new patients and doing a number of diagnostic and therapeutic procedures which we have noted on rounds. In my own mind, I have likened the work of an MA at Kiomboi to that of an intern in our hospitals at home, and when I am on morning rounds I seem to be reliving my residency years. Except when really pressed for time, all rounds are teaching rounds, and we have a retinue of MA's, nurses, and students winding along the ward like the longtime chief of surgery of Cook County Hospital, Dr. Karl Meyer, at his best!

11:10: I go now to my own office in a wing of the Ob-Gyn (obstetrics-gynecology) building, passing a long line of outpatients sitting on benches just outside my door. I tell them to wait patiently for a moment, since I have something very important to do before seeing them. I then close my door, and, putting my feet up on the desk, pour myself a cup of hot coffee from the thermos jug I carried down early in the morning. Such luxury. Outside my window I hear Pastor Kitilama leading the waiting outpatients in a hymn. The singing is a little desultory this morning. The pastor is not very vivacious even at

34

his best, and when leading singing he is not his best. He is being transferred the day after tomorrow, and Pastor Danieli Makala, a much more lively and likable young man, will be taking his place. We are in hopes that he can add a little zest to the evangelism program at the hospital.

11:15: Martha Yonitani, my office assistant, brings in the first patient, who has already been seen this morning over in the outpatient department by MA Mr. Yakobo Nehemia, and has been referred to the doctor for further disposition. Her problem is back pain, and on examination I find she has extensive scarring in the pelvis, with enlarged tubes. On further questioning, I learn that she has never had children, and that she had gonorrhea when a young girl. She is told she needs surgery for relief of her symptoms, and she agrees to return on Thursday for operation on Friday. Maybe she will come and maybe she won't. This particular problem is so common that our outpatient clinic is full of patients with this trouble. I call it our KKKK clinic, for the first letters of the Swahili words meaning backache due to gonorrhea —kiuna kinauma kutoka kisonona.

The next patient comes with the presumptive diagnosis of leprosy, but skin snips have been taken from eyebrows, ears, nose, buttocks, and a suspect lesion, and are reported as containing no acid-fast bacilli. I examine the lesion in question and can find no anesthesia. Because of the nature of this disease, I feel safe in giving a little ointment and asking the patient to return in three months for reexamination. There is not the stigma attached to the disease in this area that there is in some parts of the world, but the people are still frightened by the prospect of contracting leprosy because they have all seen the horrible end stages. Consequently they come with all

35

kinds of skin conditions, terribly worried that they have leprosy.

11:30: The next patient is a young man who needs medical clearance for acceptance to our teacher-training course at Kinampanda. He has no problems except that a routine stool examination revealed hookworm, and he has already received the one dose treatment while waiting to see me. So I sign the forms.

11:40: The following patient has bilateral cataracts, and is led in by his wife, herself nearly blind from trachoma. I explain to the man that he does indeed need an operation, but that Dr. Norquist, our eye specialist, is in Dar now, and will not be back for ten days. He wants to know if he can be made to see again, and I tell him that if the operation is successful and he is willing to wear glasses, he will be able to see very well. A slow smile spreads across his face; he speaks rapidly in his own dialect to his wife who has not understood the Swahili conversation, and she also responds with a slow warmth stealing into her face. They are a pitiful-looking couple. I examine her, too. Long-standing infection has caused a turning-in of both the lids of the left eye and the lower lid of the right, causing great irritation and scarring. I tell her through her husband that her remaining sight can be preserved if she will also come in the hospital for operations of the lids. She is dubious. The husband argues with her, then explains to me that maybe after his own surgery, she will come in. They shuffle out, the near-blind leading the blind.

11:55: The next patient is a mirror image of the first patient with the pelvic problem, except that in addition there is an element of acute disease here. I order an injection of long-acting penicillin and ask her to return in two weeks for reexamination. By that time she may be simmered down enough that she won't need surgery, or if she does come to operation, the acute infection will be somewhat under control.

12:10: The next patient is a fourteen-year-old boy with a hernia and an undescended testicle. I saw him about three months earlier, and told him to come in for admission on any Monday or Thursday. Now he has come, and our schedule for tomorrow is too full to take him. He elects to be admitted anyway, and wait for the next period, which will be on Friday.

12:15: The last patient to be seen this morning is a forty-year-old woman with a fifteen-year history of asthma. She lives in close proximity to a dispensary of ours at Ushora, and an accompanying note from the Medical Assistant tells the all-too-common story of the chronic asthmatic—multiple attacks, multiple drugs, slowly progressive dyspnea (shortness of breath) even between acute attacks. She has heard of the operation I have been doing on the neck for patients with asthma, and she comes requesting surgery. Originally interested by an article in the June 9, 1962 issue of the *Journal of the American Medical Association* by Dr. Richard Overholt of Boston, and stimulated to action by the steady procession of asthmatics in my clinic at Kiomboi, I began doing "glomectomies" (removal of a tiny body on the carotid artery in the neck) on selected cases. We have done seventeen cases, prior to this lady before me. One of them was Mr. Mangare's father, who has not had an attack in three months since surgery, whereas he had had two to four attacks a month prior to surgery. Two patients we did had severe attacks after surgery while still in the hospital. The results run the gamut, therefore, from excellent to poor. And we never know pre-operatively which patients will be benefited. I explain all this to the patient before me, and she readily agrees to the trial.

12:15: Home to dinner. Edna has been baking all

37

morning, and I catch the odor wafting from the kitchen as I come up the path. Can anyone react with an emotion other than nostalgia when he smells the odor of baking bread? It is an odor long gone from most American homes, and a whole generation has now grown up without knowing the epitome of goodness in household smells.

Edna has also prepared a roast from the haunch of a Thomson's gazelle I shot a couple of weeks ago down at Chem Chem; oh, how we suffer at meal times! Eland steaks one day, Tommy roasts the next, pork loin (wild boar) the next, curry-and-rice made of kwale birds the next. And so on. If I can go hunting once or twice a month, we live in real luxury, at least as far as meat is concerned. During the rains, we sometimes can't get off the main roads, and hunting is difficult, but during the dry season, May through November, we can go literally anywhere in the Land Rover.

1:30: Radio. I talk at length with Alpha Jacques, a registered nurse at ALM 5 (Iambi) concerning an elderly man with a hematoma (blood clot) of the liver following attempted needling of a suspected amebic abscess. Some other traffic, but nothing of importance.

2:00: Back to the office. I notice that there aren't too many patients waiting at the OPD, so I anticipate a quiet afternoon and look forward to getting some reading done in my medical journals. We have a continuing subscription to three journals, and I have done pretty well in keeping up with the progress of medicine at home. Most of the articles concern problems of little consequence to my practice here, but I remind myself that I will not be here forever.

2:05: There are four patients waiting on my private little bench. I am interrogating the first one when a breathless student knocks and comes in with the news that Sister Greta Engborg wants me to see a patient in the labor ward right away. (According to British tradition, all nurses are sisters.) I go down quickly, and find, not a great emergency, but one of the more common problems that we have to deal with in obstetrics—a tired, dehydrated, slightly toxic young woman unable to bear her child. She has been in labor for three days, and after examination I find the baby still high, but with complete cervical dilatation, and I suspect that a Cesarean section will have to be done. However, with the baby's heart tones still good, we can wait a couple of hours and get the patient in better shape for surgery.

2:30: I return to my outpatients. The first is another KKKK patient. The second is an infant with clubfeet that I have been treating for about six weeks; I send the mother to the emergency room to have an MA remove the casts so that I can recast them. The third patient is also an infant with a congenital anomaly, having a stub of a sixth finger on both hands. The bases are too broad to tie off, so I send this baby to minor surgery with a note to the nurse to get things ready. The fourth patient has disappeared somewhere and will no doubt show up in an hour or two. His card indicates he is somewhat of a hypochondriac with multiple entries of trivial or even non-existent illnesses.

2:50: I settle myself with my feet on the desk (my favorite habitus at home as well as here) with a journal, only to be interrupted again by a student with a note from Mr. Mangare concerning two new admissions on Ward E, gynecology. I go over and examine them. They seem to have been afflicted with the same disease, both having large volleyball-sized pelvic masses. One knows Swahili and one doesn't, so I get both histories through the one patient. Also I tell both of them my findings through the one woman who can speak Swahili, and before we are through, they are both giggling like schoolgirls because of the extreme similarity of history, physical findings, and projected surgical treatment. They are soon jabbering away in Kinylamba and the whole ward is laughing. They are scheduled for Friday.

3:25: I return to the labor ward and find my patient in great pain and with no evident progress, but the baby is still good and the general condition of the mother is much better, so she is immediately scheduled for surgery.

3:30: While the operating room is being prepared, I cast the feet of the baby with the clubfeet, and then resect the extra digits on the other baby. Mr. Nehemia Jakobo and a student nurse help me with both.

3:45: I go to the OR. Sister Ann Saf, a missionary nurse in her third four-year term in Tanganyika, is readying the general anesthesia equipment and supervising the setting up of the back table. Mr. Nathaniel Msambe, RN, is already scrubbed and is working on the Mayo table. One student is also scrubbed, and another running about getting sutures and other items not included in the laparotomy pack. Mr. Mangare is scrubbing.

3:50: I give the premedication intravenously (petholorfan and atropine), and start my own scrub. I take a brush from a rack on the wall, wet down my hands and arms over the sink, and squirt soap (pHisohex) on my hands by stepping on a lever on the floor. The water comes from a tank in the attic, and is chlorinated. At this time of the day it has been pleasantly warmed by the sun, whereas in the morning it is cold. I watch the preparation of the patient through the window between scrub room and OR. Everything is proceeding satisfactorily. The little clock in its wire cage tells me I have scrubbed long enough, and I back into the swinging doors and enter the room.

4:05: Mr. Msambe dresses and gloves me, and together we drape the patient. She is very apprehensive, and we try to calm her down. Mr. Msambe offers a short prayer in the patient's own dialect, and I begin the local anesthetic. I have chosen to begin with local because of the frequent violent uterine contractions. Mr. Mangare is my assistant. The incision is made and carried down to the peritoneum, the last layer before actually entering the abdomen. We cover the wound with sterile towels, and Ann Saf begins the general anesthetic, which in practically all our cases is open-drop ether. As soon as the patient begins to relax from the excitement stage, I open the peritoneum. From the beginning of the general anesthetic to the delivery of the baby, I have a safe period of perhaps ten minutes during which the baby does not get enough of the ether through the umbilical cord to depress his respirations. After ten minutes, significant anesthetization of the baby begins, and this is of course to be avoided at almost all cost. I have six minutes of the ten left, which in the average case is more than enough. And so it is in this patient. Peritoneum incised, bladder flap mobilized and pushed down, transverse incision in lower uterine segment down to the amniotic membranes, suction ready, membranes incised and opened with the fingers to the size of the uterine incision, fluid and blood aspirated, baby's head levered up gently with hand, firm pressure on the upper uterus with the other hand, and a funny little face appears in the opening in the uterus. Right shoulder, then left, and in one final movement the rest of the little fellow pops out. Mr. Mangare uses a soft bulb aspirator on the mouth and nose as I wait for the cord to stop pulsating, then two clamps and a quick cut, and the baby is on his own. He opens his eyes, then closes them quickly, no doubt alarmed at what he sees, takes a few tentative breaths, and lets out a squawk heard all over this part of the

41

hospital, meanwhile ejecting a two-foot stream of urine at Mr. Msambe, a rather routine happening!

4:30: All is well. The placenta is gently extracted, pituitrin injected into the uterus, and the layers sutured together in the reverse order in which they were incised. Another miracle of creation. Does anyone ever tire of witnessing this miracle? I don't.

I hand the baby to Greta Engborg who always comes over to help with the baby in case there is trouble. We close the abdomen.

4:55: I go back to the office, find no one waiting, and go home. Eric, our eight-year-old, is waiting patiently to practice baseball. His school is on vacation now, so all his buddies have gone home for a month and he has to settle for me.

5:30: A teacher from the primary school comes with a note to the Education Secretary in Singida, asking permission to go as a player to the national "football" (soccer) games in Dodoma next week. I promise to send the message by radio tonight.

5:35: Barbara, our six-year-old, entreats me to read her a story, which I do. Her favorite: *Heidi*. She says it makes her think of Heidi Bjurstrom, a friend in America, which makes her sad. I ask her why she wants to be sad, and she says, "It is a happy kind of sad." I have enjoyed the ability to be with my children during this last year as much as I have enjoyed anything.

6:00: Supper—soup and sandwiches. After supper another story for Barb and Eric.

7:00: To my study for a half-hour of Swahili-study. I have enjoyed my experience of learning a new language. Before coming out here, I did not anticipate learning the language, but we had been here only a few days when I realized how foolish it would be to live here for over a year and not learn to talk to the people. And how much

I *would* have missed. In the first place, it was embarrassing to be addressed by an African and have to admit to not being able to talk to him. His reaction was always one of amazement that I didn't know the language. Also it was very difficult in the wards and especially in the office when I had to hunt up an interpreter just to ask the patient a few simple questions. There have been more subtle benefits, too. There has been a gradual increase in the camaraderie with the many Africans on and near the station who speak no English or have a very limited understanding. Not that I wasn't welcomed with my fault of incommunicability; I was. But there was such a difference as my ability to speak and to hear Swahili increased. Also, I was told by other missionaries that "my stock went up" with the African staff as I learned the language because it indicated a desire to better identify with the people. I know myself how I feel about foreigners who come to the United States and live there, sometimes for years, and never learn English. In a way, it is an insult to the native-born people.

I hunt for my Swahili text amid the litter on my desk—books, pipes, Swahili readers, Eric's photographs, Barbara's hair-curlers, boxes of butterflies, marbles, parts of broken gadgets to be fixed, and so forth. Like my garage at home, into which I usually cannot even drive the car, my desk is the convenient catch-all for the entire family. Edna's kitchen is little better off, for here she must boil the drinking water, bake bread and rolls and pies and cakes, cook our meals, wash our clothes, and do all the other hundred things which make up her busy day. Here she must barter with the farmers for eggs (sometimes one or two eggs at a time), bananas, potatoes, onions, peanuts, chickens. Here she must finish the butchering of the animals I have hunted, since this is our only source of edible meat. And here she must store the supplies which come every week or two from Singida, sixty miles away.

7:30: Radio. Routine exchanges.

7:50: The kids are getting ready for bed, with a bowl of cereal as a "midnite snack" as they call it. I am in the process of reading *Conscience of a Conservative,* a rather startling treatise by Senator Barry Goldwater, a name now much in the news since Rocky's matrimonial difficulties. I must admit to a long-standing adherence to most of Goldwater's tenets, but some of his attitudes expressed concerning foreign aid and nuclear-bomb testing are a little disconcerting. However, his underlying desire to restore the federal government to its status as the servant of the people rather than their master is to be admired.

11:00: The lights go off, as they always do at 11:00, and I light up the Aladdin kerosene lamp. I become so engrossed with Barry that I don't notice the mantle blacking out until it is gone with a puff and I am in total darkness. Edna has gone to bed long ago, so I light the tiny kerosene wick lamp and leave it in the hallway and go to bed.

Sleep comes easily, here at Kiomboi. Life has been reduced to the elemental pursuits: the job to be done, the simpler interactions of a small nucleus of similar-minded people, the obtaining of food, the maintenance of the home. In the black, still night, few sounds are heard except the wind, and in the wind, the night-bird flies around and around the house with his peculiar call, and the prowling hyena voices his peculiar "arooooop." Tomorrow is not yet here, when we shall nibble away with the knife at the monstrous mountain of disease which entraps the Iramba people, the people I have come to serve.

44

4

IRAMBA-LAND

If you were to get in a small airplane at Dar es Salaam, capital city of Tanganyika on the Indian Ocean, and were to immediately climb a mile in the sky, then head slightly northwest and travel for three hundred miles as the crow flies, you would find the ground gradually getting closer and closer, and finally when you reached Kiomboi you would be at ground level. For the Iramba Plateau is over five thousand feet high.

To visualize the topography of Iramba-land, it is necessary only to picture an oval-shaped plateau, thirty-five by fifteen miles in dimension, with its edges rising almost perpendicularly from the surrounding countryside up about one thousand feet, higher in some places, lower in others. The top of the plateau is not entirely flat, but rolls gently with hills and valleys cut here and there by sand rivers that carry water only during the rainy season. Kiomboi is quite near the center of the plateau, nearer the north end, with four roads dropping off the plateau in the four points of the compass. When going over the escarpment to the north, east, or west, the roads are twisting tortuous single lanes of rock and gravel and mud, whereas the road to the south is part of the great East-West Road to Mwanza, a hard-surface (gravel) all-weather road.

On top of this mile-high plateau live the 150,000 people of the Iramba tribe. Some of the tribe has spilled over the escarpment onto the plains below, mixing there with the Sukuma, Turu, and Barabaig tribes, and another tongue of expansion extends to the west to Iambi, fifteen air miles from the edge of the escarpment. In general, the Irambas are a progressive tribe by African standards, being farmers and cattle herders. Their rate of literacy and level of civilization is high when compared to many other tribes in Tanganyika.

The average family lives in a low house made of sun-baked mud brick, the roof of interlacing saplings with mud packed on top of it. The roof is flat and is used for working and for storing corn, beans, peanuts, peppers, and sometimes other grains. The floor of the house is hard-packed earth. More and more families are introducing small tables, sitting stools, low wood and wicker beds, but many still have no furniture at all. The house forms part of the wall of an enclosure in which the livestock are kept at night for protection against lion and leopard. The corn and millet is often planted right up to the very edge of the house to utilize all the cleared space.

It is rather easy in our part of the country to obtain land for house and fields. The farmer merely locates an area not already under cultivation, builds a house, and plants as big a field as he desires. No one need be notified —no government person or agency is responsible—no deed nor bill of sale. (No financing, no closing costs, no earnest money, no taxes, no insurance!) In other words, the land is free for the taking—as much as you want— and there is more than enough land for all. There are approximately eleven million people in Tanganyika, a country of unbelievable size, a country which measures six hundred fifty air miles from east-to-west boundaries, and five hundred twenty miles north-to-south! A map of Tanganyika laid on a map of the United States would entirely cover our midwestern states of North Dakota, South Dakota, Iowa, Minnesota, Wisconsin, Illinois, Indiana, and Michigan. (It is startling at first to realize the immensity of the continent of Africa. Within its boundaries can be accommodated the entire United States, all of Europe—excluding Russia—all of India, and all of China.)

Most families have only a very few acres under cultivation, the average in Iramba-land being two acres under food crops such as millet and corn, and one and a half acres under cash crops such as peanuts and beans. It is an ironic fact that a country which is composed of more than ninety percent farmers, with great empty lands, cannot grow enough food to feed itself. It is true that little severe hunger is known in Tanganyika at the present time, but there was a famine in Turu-land just to the south of us just this year, and grain donated by other countries has been given out by the ton. There is little foresight exercised. When drought or flood reduces the yield in one year, there is hunger the next. The government has tried to force storage of food during good years by building storage silos, but great pressure has to be exerted on the people to fill them, and for the most part they stand as empty monuments to a good idea.

The average monthly income in Tanganyika is said to be only about $2.50 a month, but this figure is somewhat too low for Iramba-land. And it fails to take into account the fact that the Iramba man raises his own food, and what he wants or needs in the way of other necessities he also takes from the land or barters for. His houses rise up anywhere there are good soil for building blocks and saplings for the roof. His meat is from his own chickens and cows and goats. The average Iramba is not a poor man, at least not in this society. His necessities are few, his

47

luxuries are nonexistent, and for the most part what he needs he can buy by selling a cow or two from his walking bank account. Although not so much in Iramba-land as in more primitive areas, a man's wealth is still likely to be measured by the number of cows, goats, and sheep he owns, rather than by the size of his house or landholding. For as we have seen, land is obtainable in any amount merely by moving onto it and clearing it, and the size of the house depends only on how many people need to live in it.

The farms are small because most of the land is still worked by hand—the ground broken with the hoe, the seed sown by hand, and the harvesting done by hand—head by head of millet, ear by ear of corn—and carried back to a basket on the ground when the hands are full. It takes little imagination to estimate how long it takes to harvest an acre in this way. Added to this difficulty is the fact that the people come out of the fields in the early afternoon because they didn't eat enough to keep them going, and it is easy to see why food is not over-abundant. A vicious circle is set up—too little food, therefore too little work, therefore too little food, and so forth.

One of the major problems in Iramba-land today is that of increasing the productivity of the people and the land. It is not so much that the people are lazy as it is their philosophy of what constitutes a day's work. By American standards, the workday is very short on the farm—as it is in practically every other job also.

The farmers must be convinced that fertilization is desirable and that merely moving to an unfarmed plot is not the answer to good soil conservation. They must be encouraged to be a little more enterprising—to borrow small sums to get basic tools in order to produce more—for money is available, from local and central governments, and from farm and missionary cooperatives.

For the educated Iramba, things are somewhat different. There are limited fields at present, if he wishes to remain in Iramba-land. He may become a nurse, a teacher, a pastor, or a medical assistant. If he aspires to other fields, such as business, law, engineering, or scientific disciplines, he will not find employment in Iramba-land since there are no places as yet for those talents. He would be welcomed in the bigger cities, especially in the government, but under present circumstances it would be unthinkable to, say, set up a law office in Iramba-land for the private practice of law. There are no businesses to buy, except those owned by Indians, and he would have no capital to start his own. Besides, and even more important, the average educated African considers "shop-keeping" demeaning.

As education draws increasing numbers of youngsters into the potential middle class, new jobs will open up in smaller and smaller towns, and it is hoped that merely obtaining a fourth or eighth grade education will not remain the end by any means. In Iramba-land education now is still almost entirely at mission schools. Before the missionaries came there was *no* education. Now there are eighty-one schools on the Iramba plateau, with an average enrollment of one hundred students per school. However, seventy-six of the schools are concerned only with grades one through four, and no secondary schools (high schools) exist at all. Therefore only the exceptional students go on for "higher" education in the few high schools which exist elsewhere in Tanganyika.

One is able to see that the chance of obtaining the equivalent of a college education is extremely remote, and then only in foreign countries, since no universities exist in Tanganyika. With no personal or family income from which to draw, college education is always on direct one hundred percent scholarships. There are a few Iramba men now studying in England and America for the ministry and in general courses. While the ministers will be absorbed into the church here, the others may end up in the service of the government. As yet there are no African doctors from or in Iramba-land, but one student entered the University of Minnesota medical school in the fall of 1963, which would qualify him to practice medicine in mid-1968. He presumably will come back to Iramba-land, possibly to be employed at the Kiomboi Hospital, since his expenses are being paid by the Lutheran Church.

In many ways, Iramba-land reminds the American of the rural pattern in the United States a hundred years ago. Almost everyone makes his living from the land. Those who don't, came from farms. Money for education is scarce. We have seen that once an education is obtained, the number of fields to go into are limited. And there is a reluctance to go back to the old homestead even if an opportunity exists there, and it usually doesn't. But the pattern of family life is there for the vast majority of people. Family and clan ties are close, and a reward or an insult to one member is felt by all. And all share in the wages of a high-earning member. Nephews and uncles and cousins frequently request "loans" from our nurses and medical assistants, not intending to pay them back. And whole families will move into a relative's house for weeks and months at a time if they are down on their luck.

Decisions are practically never made by an individual, but are a family, clan, or even community affair. Indeed, that is one of the biggest problems in Africa today—to get each individual to think for himself, rather than to have to call together the elders to sit and talk for hours or days. This spills over into affairs concerning personal liberty. In the issue of the *Journal of the American Medical Association* for May 18, 1963, G. K. Higgins wrote:

The emerging democracies of Africa, for example, face years of unrest by reason of the absence of individuals, organizations, and institutions having traditions of personal liberty and representing sources of power outside the government. . . . There is an almost total lack of independent thinking on matters of personal liberty. There is a very real danger that influence, independent of government [i.e. universities and newspapers], will not develop in these new countries and consequently no source of strength and influence to check and resist the power of the state can develop.

It has been truly said that it is better to discuss a problem without deciding it than to decide a problem without discussing it, but this axiom is carried to the extreme in this culture. Church meetings bog down, roads remain unimproved, schools go without teachers, while the discussions go on forever. This pattern is beginning to break down, of course, and not entirely without deleterious effects on the individuals concerned.

With regard to the politics of this new nation, I do not intend to say much. I was there during the year that Tanganyika got its independence from England and witnessed the latter parts of the mass exodus of the British government officials. At the local level, government was entirely administered by young Africans of the TANU party (Tanganyika African National Union), the police chief and his officers were all Africans, the postmaster and his staff were Africans, and so forth.

I have been asked whether or not there were enough trained people to take over the functions of government with all its ramifications. I must say, and the many honest Africans that I talked to agreed—no, there weren't enough. Many of the positions left vacant by the English were filled by woefully inept people. Fortunately, the higher positions in government seemed for the most part exceptionally well-filled. President Julius Nyerere (pronounced Nyuh-raré-ee) is a solid, intelligent, forward-looking chief executive. He has steered Tanganyika through these trying times with little hint of the troubles in many another African republic. He has made a special continuing effort to convince his people that with the coming of independence the African must work harder, not less hard; that in order to enjoy the privileges of freedom one must also accept the responsibilities—a very mature concept, indeed, and one that is difficult for many Africans to comprehend. An unfortunate tendency for many Africans is to blame all their troubles on the white man, despite the fact that of the thousands of years of their existence, the white man has been in Africa in a ruling capacity for a mere half-century. But President Nyerere tells them over and over: "Mnapiga uvivu—you are lazy. Don't you know that the progressive nations aren't lucky—they are industrious—we have been asleep for centuries—now let's wake up. Tufanye kazi—tujitoe—let's get to work, let's do it ourselves."

In summary, our sketch of Iramba-land depicts a mile-high plateau, dry half the year, green half the year, with 150,000 people, almost all farmers, who have gradually pulled themselves up (being pushed and pulled also) out of heathenism, ignorance, poverty, and sickness, into the twentieth century. This is where Kiomboi Lutheran Hospital finds itself, in 1963 with overtones of nationalism and undercurrents of racism.

5

THE HOSPITAL—TUESDAY

6: 30: It is just barely getting light when we are jarred ruthlessly by the monster in the closet. Sitting nearly on the equator, we are the victims of a seven o'clock sunrise and a seven o'clock sunset every day of the year. Our African friends are incredulous when they are told that in our summertime at home we have days during which there are eighteen hours of daylight, and they are even more startled to learn that there are places in the far north where the sun never does go down for several months at a time and furthermore doesn't shine at all during other months!

7: 00: Because of early surgery, I am dressed and ready to go to work by the time radio is called.

7: 10: Breakfast. Eric stumbles sleepily to the table and asks when are we going hunting again? I tell him maybe tomorrow afternoon, if I can get away, but don't count on it. Fred Malloy at the school wants to try out a new .375 Magnum he just bought from Doug Augustine at Kinampanda and thinks he knows where there are some eland that haven't been hunted for over a year. Sure would like to go. We're low on meat.

7: 30: Fridaeli, a student nurse, is leading our private morning vespers as I come into the minor surgery room.

On surgery days we of the OR staff do not attend the general chapel service because that would set us an hour behind, so we conduct a five-minute service of our own. It is a rather different and pleasant way to greet the morning than most of us are used to at home.

7:35: The patient is already in the operating room. She is to have a glomectomy; I listen to her lungs to determine if she is at this time having any asthmatic wheezing; she has none. Sometimes in these cases there is an immediate response to surgery and wheezing heard preoperatively is not heard postoperatively.

7:50: I start the local anesthetic, make the incision over the right side of the neck, carry it down through the successive layers of fascia to the carotid artery, search for the superior thyroid artery, ligate it, and using it as a tractor, rotate the bifurcation so that I can see the backside, identify the glomus, and dissect it free of the vessel. Closing the wound is done quickly with interrupted sutures and the skin with clips. There are no problems and no complications. Some go easily, some with more difficulty.

8:25: Mr. Mangare and I unscrub. The staff and students are going to their wards from the chapel, and the corridors are not unpleasantly full of talk and laughter. A few ambulatory patients are strolling about. A day laborer in the courtyard between Wards A and B is sweeping up the leaves with a short branch, as Mr. Mangare and I go out to see a few patients between cases. The wind blows coldly and we are glad we left on our heavy cotton surgical gowns. The husband of a patient stops me to tell me they have run out of food and money and he cannot leave the woman in the hospital any longer. She is far from well and I tell him so. He repeats his problem. I tell him to go to the matron-in-charge to see if some arrangements can be made. He goes off unhappily. If he is truly destitute, some solution can always be found; if he is merely trying to get out of paying any more money for his wife, he will be treated accordingly. The African staff can nearly always make the distinction correctly and fairly.

8:40: I put the spinal anesthetic into our second patient, tip her into a head down position, and take the blood pressure. As the anesthetic sets, I take the pressure frequently, and after about ten minutes I see that there has been little change. I relinquish my seat to Miss Ukende and rescrub for three minutes, watching the patient through the window. By the time I am regowned, Mr. Msambe and Mr. Mangare have draped the patient and we are ready. This is the patient from Ward E with the huge pelvic mass. Miss Ukende prays with the patient and we begin.

8:55: The incision climbs the belly to the umbilicus and the muscles can be seen stretched and thinned out by the tumor mass beneath. A movement with the scalpel handle separates them in the midline, and Mr. Mangare is there with forceps to pick up the peritoneum. I pick up opposite him and cautiously incise the sheet of glistening white-blue tissue, watching for adherent tumor mass or bowel. The mass is an irregular, cystic tumor, benign to our first glance. Loops of bowel are adherent to it, but come away easily with sharp dissection. Finally, I can reach behind it and free it bluntly with the hand and deliver it into the incision. It still looks benign. Now visualization of the uterus and other ovary is possible and they look normal. A very firm decision must be made at this point. Surgically it would be possible to remove just the right tube and ovarian tumor without disturbing the uterus or the other side. The patient looks to be about forty and has had six children, two of whom are alive; she, like practically all Africans, does not know how old she is, nor can she guess. If this tumor, however, is malignant, it would be very poor treatment not to do a total excision of the pelvic organs. The patient is awake, and quite alert. I ask Mr. Msambe, an Iramba man, to explain to the patient that we should take out her uterus, but if she is violently opposed, we will not. She hedges, says it must be God's decision. Not being God, I hesitate to take over that function, but a decision must be made. We free up the organs to the point of not being able to retrace our steps by clamping and cutting the uterine arteries. We are now committed. With the tumor in the basin, I put on a second pair of sterile gloves, use some instruments on the back table which will not be needed again, and incise the tumor. About three quarts of yellow fluid flood the basin from one section, and another quart from several smaller loculations. An orange-size mass remains. I incise it, and the knife grates like it was going through the heart of a cabbage. The feeling is unmistakably that of a cancerous growth. I look carefully for signs of spread within the cystic parts and can see none. I toss the instruments, now contaminated with cancer cells, into the basin and hand it to Ann Saf. She strips off my outer gloves and we now are ready to close. This was a close call, since statistics indicate that perhaps fifty percent of all ovarian cancers are bilateral from the start, and removal of just the one ovary which is cancerous leaves half of the cases with assurance of "recurrence."

We resuture the floor of the pelvis and then close the abdomen. The patient asks to see the tumor and sucks in her breath in a characteristic Iramba gesture. There is no word in the Bantu languages for cancer, so we tell her that she had a very bad disease which we have removed. Her response is simple, heartwarming, sincere: "Thank you."

10: 05: We unscrub again, and this time head for my office for that indispensable mid-morning cup. A whole family of Indians from a Kiomboi shop accosts me outside the hospital and with a faint trace of obsequiousness ask to be seen. I find it difficult to conceal a certain amount of irritation. They have a perverse habit of coming four and five at a time with all manner of trivial complaints, expecting miracles (I suppose we should be grateful for the compliment to our healing powers), and always on surgery days. And they are no different from Americans or Africans in that they are greatly disappointed if they don't get a "shot," for whatever ails them. Simple advice or instructions are never accepted, and one feels quite the charlatan giving them some vitamins just to finally get them out of the office! They always bypass the out-patient department, coming directly to the doctor (paying for that privilege, it must be said in all fairness), and will walk right by a line of patient Africans and come right in the office after a peremptory knock. I am still not reconciled to this, even though they pay Sh/15 (about two dollars), compared to the half shilling paid by the average African patient. I ask them if there are any problems that cannot wait till tomorrow, and they say no, they suppose not. They leave, and we go in for our cup of coffee, beginning to feel guilty for being so brusque.

10:20: We scrub again, this time for a large direct hernia, but without any unusual features or problems. This is also done under spinal anesthesia, an ideal anesthetic for lower abdominal cases. The sun is high now, and shines so brightly through the skylight that we do not need the lights on. The brightness of the OR has enabled us to work many a time when the light plant has been malfunctioning. It has also been a boon for photography of unusual surgical conditions.

11:10: I start writing up the cases from the morning's work so far, sitting on the anesthesia stool in the main OR. The nurses are busily changing the linen on the table, collecting the bloody sponges off the rack to be washed out, sterilized, and used again.

A student is vigorously wet-mopping the concrete floor, curiously unconcerned with the fact that she had only a thin gruel for breakfast, has only one pair of shoes and some plastic sandals, has no indoor plumbing at her dormitory, has one bare 60-watt light bulb and that for four hours a day, will have no dinner this noon except tea and a handful of peanuts or possibly a few handsful of cornmeal mush, and will then have the same meal again tonight along with a gravy of onions or cabbage. All she knows is that her lot is immeasurably improved over what she had at home, and the future looks even brighter. When she graduates she will be a "registered worker," that magical designation which will separate her forever from her past. Her salary will be stipulated by the government, and will be the same over all of Tanganyika except that in some mission hospitals the cash remunerations is perhaps fifteen percent less, with the difference being made up in housing and more pleasant working conditions. She is a grade-school graduate, sixteen years old, from Chagga-land, and lived in the very shadow of Mt. Kilimanjaro till she came down here. She knows three languages—Swahili, English, and her own Chagga dialect. She is learning nursing in the English language, at the order of the central government; most missionaries would actually rather teach in Swahili in order to avoid the inevitable confusions and misconceptions which arise when teaching in English, which in fact is a foreign language despite the fact that it is taught for at least four years in upper primary school.

At the present time all higher education (any instruction above the grades) is in English. For one thing, Swahili developed originally as a means of communication between the Arab traders and the East Africans, and it has literally no words for any technical or scientific objects or ideas except those taken over from other languages, notably English. For example, a basic word in industry, "machine," has been taken from the English and "Swahili-ized" into *mashini* (ma-shin'-i). This could be done with the thousands of words necessary to study physics, nursing, mathematics, and so forth, but the resulting jargon would be laughable. It is indeed interesting to listen to, say, Sig Waltenburg at the mission garage telling a mechanic how to do something: "Bwana, funga nut juu ya bolt, na weka zote ndani ya carburetor, halafu waweza kupima horn tena gear-shift." It can be really hilarious. We call this type of conversations "Kiswinglish." Another example, copied from a notice on the bulletin board in the operating workroom: "Namna ya ku-sterilize kwa pressure cooker kubwa." ("Way to sterilize with the big pressure cooker.")

11:20: Our student is finishing mopping the floor and holds open the swinging doors for another student to push in the next patient. A pair of black feet, horny and calloused from years of walking in the dust and thorns, precede the rest of the patient on the rolling "trolley." This old man is an old friend of mine. He came into the hospital six weeks ago with a both-bone fracture of the forearm, which Joe Norquist manipulated under general anesthesia and got the bones to lie in an almost normal anatomical position. He was casted from shoulder to fingers, and we decided to send him home to see if he would maintain the alignment. Two weeks ago he came *sans* cast, claiming he had tired of it and had soaked and hacked it off with his machete. Of course, the arm looked like it had two elbows when he returned, and our only course now is to operate on it and put the pieces back together.

11:25: I find the transverse part of the first rib with

the long needle deep in the hollow of the neck above the clavicle, and inject five cubic centimeters of xylocaine in three distinctly separate areas, a technique which might appall some anesthesiologists, but which has worked very well for me in these very thin people in whom I find it difficult to ascertain good nerve sensations indicative of accurate placement of the needle.

11:30: While the anesthetic is setting, I go out on the wards again to see some patients. Medical Assistant Sampson Paulo has made complete rounds of all the patients, and we confer for a few moments. He wants me to see a Barabaig patient whom we have skin grafted, covering his left forearm and upper arm with skin from his legs. He is an epileptic and his body is covered with healed burns, in addition to the arm which we are working on. Contractures of burn scars of the knees have pulled his heels up against his buttocks, and one of his feet is nearly a solid mass of scar tissue without recognizable toes. Three fingers on one hand and two on the other have also been pulled by scar tissue down into the palms. The nurses have undressed the left arm so that I can see it. It is a patchwork of new skin, with thin red lines between each section, and I consider it now at the stage where we can leave it open. We also discuss the possibility of straightening one of his legs surgically so that he can at least get up on crutches.*

11:50: I check the sensation in the arm of the old man in the OR, and find it nearly gone. We scrub, prep, drape, and begin the incision along the shaft of the ulna. We know from the X-rays that the fracture in both bones is nearly transverse so that it should be an ideal case to fix with a long rod down the marrow canal. This is soon seen to be true, and without great difficulty a thin Rush

* This patient did later have both legs straightened surgically and was being taught to walk again.

rod is driven through the proximal bone, through the bent elbow, then back down across the fracture site into the distal fragment. This wound is closed and a separate incision made along the radius. This bone is then reduced relatively easily into normal alignment, and, lacking the tools to affix a bone graft, we plate it and pack around it cancellous bone which has been taken from the pelvic bone through a third incision down there. A long-arm cast finishes the procedure. Things have gone smoothly and a near-optimum operation has been done, thanks entirely to the munificence of the people of Eau Claire, Wisconsin, who a year ago responded generously and with alacrity to a plea for orthopedic instruments and equipment.

1:15: It has been a long time since breakfast, and I can feel those pleasantly uncomfortable rumblings announcing dinnertime. Ann Saf and I agree to reconvene at 2:15 for the final case of the day.

2:15: We start the last case. I have given a larger dose of anesthetic than usual and have tipped the patient down a little more than usual, in order to obtain a higher level of anesthesia. We are dealing with a huge abdominal tumor again, and in addition, there is a gigantic spleen which I would like to remove, requiring a very high level of anesthesia, preferably at least to the nipple line. Even then there will be some discomfort when the spleen is peeled off the undersurface of the diaphragm. I have given some ephedrine by hypo in order to maintain the expected drop in blood pressure, but it soon becomes obvious that something else must be done, and quickly. The blood pressure is dropping out of sight and the patient is becoming restless and nauseous. I break scrub and inject a full cubic centimeter of ephedrine slowly intravenously and am rewarded with an almost instantaneous rise in the B/P (blood pressure). I rescrub, and we begin the operation. Ann Saf is watching the B/P and pulse, and Miss Ukende is hooking up the suction amidst a tangle of hoses and wires from wall and transformer and the cold light over the operating table.

3:00: The first part of the operation has gone smoothly and as I resuture the pelvic floor I ask for a check on the patient's condition. Like a brief countdown on a rocket, Ann gives me the information I need, and we decide to go ahead with the splenectomy. I incise the skin, fascia, and peritoneum as one layer, facilitated by the relaxation and thinness of the abdominal wall up to the lower border of the ribs on the left. I remind myself of a truism oft quoted by Dr. Peter Rosi and hundreds of surgeons following in his footsteps at Cook County Hospital: the incision heals from side to side, not end to end, so that a long incision heals as rapidly as a short one. The lower end of the spleen has been in our lower abdominal incision, but the upper end is at the extreme apex of the abdominal cavity, so that although with a little legerdemain we might have succeeded in clamping and tying the lower part of the spleen, we could not possibly have *safely* gotten at the major vessels and the upper pole.

3:15: Trouble. Working posteriorly with the fingers, I have succeeded in freeing up all except the very tip of the spleen where it normally has only filmy attachments to the diaphragm (if any). Here at the tip, I find a hard, bony calcification of the spleen which is densely adherent to the diaphragm. Blood is oozing slowly from the previously dissected area, so that I cannot afford much time to ponder. There is a high chance of perforating the diaphragm if I continue the dissection, and an even higher chance of uncontrollable bleeding if I don't. I continue the dissection, blindly because of the depth of the organ, gently working my fingers along between the calcification and the under surface of the diaphragm. I listen intently for the telltale gush of air. The patient is restless. She can feel an aching sensation in the left shoulder, referred from the operative area. The pulse is still strong; I can feel the heart on my knuckles through the one-eighth-inch-thick diaphragmatic muscle. Pauline Swanson comes to the door to tell me to be sure to stop to see the teacher's baby before I go home. I grunt, knowing I will forget unless I am reminded again. One just cannot divert one's mind to memory work in situations like this. My children tell me I keep my brains in my pocket because of all those little notes to myself.

3:35: With a "slurrrp," the spleen nearly jumps from the wound. I pack three large pads into the void and we all visibly relax. No one but I, and possibly Mangare, realize how close we came to real trouble. The splenic pedicle is handled, and three pads removed slowly. A few "pumpers" greet us and are quickly ligated on long Mixter forceps.

4:15: Mr. Mangare and I have worked from opposite ends of the wound and the abdomen is now closed. The patient's B/P has slowly slid off to 70/60 despite ephedrine, and I order a plastic flask of a Dutch plasma expander called "onkovertin" (dextran) to be started intravenously, wishing we had blood available. I have started the slow ball a-rolling to initiate a "walking" blood bank, but we have gotten nowhere yet. There is too much apathy even among the staff, let alone the potential donors. And there is good reason for pessimism. An attempt was made a number of years ago to start a blood bank, but the response was absolutely nil. The African will practically never give blood even to his own kin, and to give to a stranger is an entirely foreign concept. I am hoping that the general climate of change here in Iramba-land will have caused a reshuffling in this realm also.

4:20: To my amazement, I remember the teacher's baby with the convulsions. Knowing I can probably do nothing constructive, I nevertheless go over to see it. It is in the midst of a generalized convulsion, and I stand by helplessly, trying to console the mother. When the convulsions stop, I examine the baby and find nothing new. I can neither add nor subtract from the situation.

4:30: Back to the office, glance at the empty benches, and breathe a sigh of relief. Greta hears my footsteps and asks me to see an OB, which I do quickly, finding no great problem. Her first two babies were by forceps and her third one by a more normal way, so the midwives are understandably concerned this time also. I reassure both patient and nurses, wishing I could feel as confident as I sound.

5:30: I go over the mail when I get home. A letter from my parents, another from the Retallicks, and a third from the Eau Claire-Dunn-Pepin County Medical Society, addressed simply to "Dr. Dibble, Lutheran Medical Mission, Tanganyika." This is approximately comparable to addressing a letter to "Rev. Gravdahl, Lutheran Church, Wisconsin." The letter itself is very welcome, indicating in it that I am still a member in good standing in the local society, the fees having been "forgiven" for the year.

6:00: We have been invited down to one of the nurses' houses for supper, and as we are about to leave, we encounter a smiling redheaded stranger of about twenty-one or twenty-two years of age. He introduces himself as Dick Latchaw, a University of Minnesota student in Africa for a two-month period to study the sociological aspects of medical practice. We show him where to clean up and offer him supper, which he readily accepts. He then informs us that his rented Volkswagen is stranded thirteen miles down the road with two flats, and all his gear (including passport) is inside. I know the area where the car is, and suspect that it is safe enough, but we plan to go get the gear later anyway.

6:20: We go down to the nurses' house, where Jean Johnson has an Italian dinner prepared, salt sticks and all. No spumoni, however!

7:20: I leave the dinner early in order to get on the radio, then spend a couple of hours talking to Dick about his work. He is concerned about the conflicting "facts" he has received from various sources in Tanganyika. He is reminded of the six blind men from Hindustan, all examining a different part of the elephant and coming to entirely different conclusions as to the nature of the beast, not realizing that they each have only a partial truth and therefore are partly right but entirely wrong. It is a fact of African medical life that despite efforts to "governmentalize" medical services, over half the hospital beds in Tanganyika now are maintained by missions. With this brutal fact in mind, the central government can ill afford to make the existence of the missionaries too difficult, and indeed are leaning over backward to help the missions continue in "business." This is a bilateral arrangement, since the missions desperately need help from the government, financial and moral.

10:30: We decide to go for Dick's gear, although there will be no possibility of getting the car itself. It takes us about an hour. Everything is intact. The car is in an uninhabited area down the Sekenke Road and the likelihood of anyone coming by at night would be remote; besides, in general the people in Iramba-land are honest by nature and respectful of other people's property. There are thieves, of course, but the ordinary passerby would not even think of breaking into a stalled car.

11:30: The lights are all out when we return. The generator is shut off so we light our little kerosene lamps and get ready for bed.

12:00 midnight: I am not quite asleep when I hear voices coming up the path from the hospital. A shifting bright white light accompanies the voices, and soon I am awake enough to realize I am wanted. Soon the greeting "hodi" at the window, and the two students inform me that a baby is in the Emergency Room with a peanut in his throat. I groan inwardly and outwardly.

12:15: "What is the baby's trouble, mother?"

"He has swallowed a peanut."

"What kind of trouble does he have?"

"He coughs."

"Any other trouble?"

"He collapses."

"How old is the baby?"

"He was born last year." (He looks to be about two.)

"How did he get a peanut, mother?"

"I gave it to him."

"Mother, my children did not get peanuts to eat until they were five years old. Did you not know it is dangerous?"

No answer.

I listen to the baby's lungs. Breath sounds are good, without collapse of either lung. The baby coughs occasionally. When crying, he seems to be a little bluish around the lips. When quiet, he breathes normally.

12:45 AM: I decide we had better bronchoscope the baby. This is not a decision entered into lightly, in our situation, as will become clear. I send a runner to Ann Saf's to get the key to the instrument cupboard. I decide to try it without suction, hoping to avoid starting up the light plant. We prepare things by the light of a kerosene pressure lamp.

66

1:05 AM: The runner returns with the key, with Pauline Swanson in close pursuit. Together we get out the bronchoscopes and cords. One of the students goes to my office across the courtyard to get the handle to the otoscope, which will be our power source.

1:45: The baby is held down and I do a direct visualization of the vocal chords, hoping against hope that the foreign body will be visible high in the pharynx or at least above the vocal chords. It isn't. (It never is!) I slide a scope in, visualize the trachea, and am somewhat surprised not to see the peanut. Before I can adequately examine the rest of the bronchial tree, liquid secretions begin to form and I reluctantly back out.

2:05 AM: I send a runner to rout out Eliasafi, our chief maintenance man, to start the generator so we will have power for the suction machine.

2:15: The lights blaze on. We check the suction. It works fine. I reintroduce the three and a half millimeter scope and try to get the suction tip down. It is too big. I try it on a four mm scope, and it passes readily. I remove the three and a half mm scope from the baby, and quickly find that the four mm scope will not pass the vocal chords. Again that vague feeling of frustration, of not being able to do just what one wants to. I visualize the chords with a laryngoscope and slide the suction tip down as far as I can, then take it out and slide in the smaller scope. I repeat this operation several times, until I have assured myself that no foreign body is within the trachea, and until I have thoroughly traumatized the vocal chords with the multiple manipulations.

2:45: I am thoroughly unhappy. There has been no improvement in the baby's condition. He has a cough which has got to be due to a foreign body. But there is none there. The mother is worried. I am worried. I am tired. As I sit thinking and waiting, the baby falls asleep, breathing easily. This decides me. We quit for the night. It is just barely possible that the baby has a developing pneumonia and not a foreign body at all.

3:10 AM: I stop by Eliasafi's house on the way home and ask him to turn off the light plant. He commiserates with me on my night's work, and as I walk up the path, I can hear his battered old jeep cough to life, and the thought crosses my mind that there must be a peanut in the fuel injection system.

3:15: The lights go off as I enter the house, so I grope my way to bed.

6

THE BUSH

Safari. White hunter. Big game hunting.

These are magic words to millions of people throughout the world, and very few would turn down the opportunity to go with gun or camera into the bush country of East Africa. There is an aura of excitement that surrounds these words.

The picture that comes to most minds when Africa is mentioned is one of rain forests, steaming jungles, gorillas, and Tarzan swinging through the trees on long vines! Parts of Africa are like this, of course, especially in the low countries like the Congo and the Cameroons, but most of Africa is not like this at all. Hardly any of East Africa, for example, is "jungle." It is "bush country." And Kiomboi lies right in the heart of rather typical bush country—country which can be big or close, wet or dry, green or brown, inviting or forbidding. We have seen this bush country in all its moods. We live in it and have come to love it so that it now lives in us and will never be forgotten. What is this "bush" that is all about us? What are its characteristics?

If you drive along a main road, gravel or black top, the bush stretches out to the horizons in all directions. It is brown-yellow in the dry season, and green-yellow in

the rains. There are areas of open plain and country
with only enough low bushes and scattered acacias and
thorn trees to prevent it from being a totally open plain.
Then there are areas of thicker bush, with the trees and
bushes close enough together that you can see only a
hundred yards or so back into it unless you are on a hill
or a ridge. Then there are areas so thick that only occasional game trails penetrate the dense thickets, and
you could miss seeing an elephant only a few feet back
of the road.

Driving on a ridge through bush country, you look out
over a country so vast that it cannot be described, only
compared. It is like the vastness of our north country in
the United States, or of the desert country in the West.
But there is a striking difference here—the distances are
so great, and the terrain changes in form so much, that
you have the feeling of being in several countries at
the same time. On the Isanzu ridge you can see hundreds
of square miles of dense to moderately dense bush off to
the north. Across the miles of bush you can see the valley of the Sibiti River: open plains, dry washes, the
sluggish river itself, and thousands of animals. And
across the plains you see the escarpments of the Masai
highlands and the Mbulu plateau. From the same ridge,
you need only turn around to see the mountains of the
Wanisanzu: sharp cliffs, green mountains, rocks and
rocks and more rocks, rocks piled and shaped by God in
some places and seemingly by the devil in others. Here
is the bulldog, big as a house, with his tongue hanging
out so realistically that you can almost see the drool.
Over there is the Roman helmet, big as a four-story
building, with horsehair crest and cheek-protectors.
And there is a half-loaf of bread, partly sliced, the size
of a barn. Over there is a tangled jumble of rocks, perched
one on top of another, half-balanced on a pinhead, ready

to fall. Another slab of rock the size of a football field seems in the act of sliding, and instinctively you shy away from a rock which has no doubt been "sliding" for thousands of years. And you can climb halfway to the top of "Cross Rock," on which Bob Ward has placed a white cross against the sky. The cross of Jesus must hold those rocks in place, because if you stand under them you get that panicky feeling that nothing is holding them up! As you drive along this ridge, watching the bush below, you cannot resist naming all the many fantastically shaped formations.

But, back to the bush. When driving through it, you can leave the road almost anywhere during the dry season, and almost nowhere during the rains. This is characteristic of true bush country. In the dry season, the ground is hard, almost rock-like, being dried clay for the most part. The grass is short, yellow, dead, and when driven over leaves a track which persists to the end of the dry season. Many times I have come on tracks that I myself made months before.

In driving directly through the bush, you can find passages almost everywhere; only occasionally do you find yourself in a *cul-de-sac* and have to back up and try a new approach. The thorn trees and bush crowd in frequently on all sides, and you can hear the screech of thorns along the top and sides of the car from time to time. It is in this type of bush that you find impala, eland, and hartebeeste. Occasionally you come on zebra and wild boar usually going to and from the grassy plains where they feed. Here you see the towering giraffes feeding on the tender tops of the acacia trees. And here you find lions skulking through the tall grass, or lying in the shade of a thorn tree, or (in some areas like Manyara) lying along the lower limbs of a big thorn tree or wild fig. The elephant makes his home in the densest bush, walking right through it as if it didn't exist, traveling miles every day in search of food and water. The rhino takes cover in this bush, standing stupidly in front of the Land Rover, sniffing with his sensitive nose, and peering near-sightedly in the direction of the sound with his notoriously weak eyes.

All of these animals will be found occasionally out on the plains with the Thomson's gazelles, wildebeeste, Grant's gazelles, and zebras, but their real home is in the bush, where in the flash of a white-flagged tail or the thunder of giant feet they can disappear as the Pied Piper's children vanished into the mountain.

If you walk through this bush, you will see two other denizens which will elude you if you are driving. These are the Cape buffalo and the leopard, both of which have such sensitive powers of hearing and smell that it is rare to see them from the car. But if you walk slowly through the bush, carefully stepping over sticks and branches, you may flush a leopard from a tree, as I have done twice, or from long grass as I did once. And if you enter the densest bush of all, impenetrable to a car, and walk extremely slowly and quietly, you may be able to approach close enough to the most dangerous animal in the bush—the Cape buffalo. If you are really careful and really lucky, you may hear them first—a snort or low bellow, not unlike a cow—and you can then check the wind and the terrain and approach on hands and knees to good shooting range. Usually though, you are seen or heard or smelled long before you sight the buffalo, and you catch a glimpse of black rumps disappearing through the undergrowth, for the buffalo probably has the most sensitive combination of sight, smell, and hearing of any of the inhabitants of the bush. Wound one, and you've got Problems, and that starts with P and that rhymes with T which stands for Trouble. He will snort and bellow and paw the ground and be on top of you while you're raising your gun. Or he will disappear down the game trail and then wait for you beside the trail, the dreaded "buffalo hook."

Mostly, we walk the more open bush where trouble is not spelled with a capital letter. The ground is hard and dusty, and in some places the tsetse flies whine around our heads. The trails crisscross in apparently aimless fashion and we don't usually follow them, especially since we aren't out walking unless we have already spotted our quarry. Stop and listen—the wind rustles the dry grass, and the thorn trees bend in the breeze. The black and white crows sail overhead, cawing loudly; the doves coo; a kwale bird calls raucously in the distance if it is evening. Vultures, always overhead, soar silently. The weaver birds' little grass nests dip and sway from where they hang on the very tips of the branches. Except for the birds, the stillness is unbroken. The sky is a deep blue, with no clouds. The equatorial sun is burning in intensity, and this, along with the wind and the dust, dries your mouth and nose in minutes. Your skin is dry, yet it will give off quarts of water in hours through insensible, unnoticed perspiration.

This is the bush. Unchanged for uncounted centuries. Big. Dry. Hot. Brown. Dusty. Dangerous.

Then the rains come. And just before the rains, big red flowers with a single slender green stalk push up through the dust and explode in a riot of red filaments flecked with yellow gold—fragile-looking, the size of a fist or bigger—in the half-shade of a nearly leafless thorn tree. With the rains, every yellow blade of grass comes to life, and the bush is transformed in weeks into a lush green carpet of tall grass, with old tracks obliterated, and old dry water holes now brimming with life-giving water. The baobabs leaf out, partly hiding the hideously

73

dwarfed branches, and now look like a child's drawing of a tree instead of the devil's own handiwork. The rock-strewn ridges lose their desolate appearance as the grass grows high and hides the smaller rocks.

Once or twice a day the thundering black clouds come out of the east, with roaring winds and tons of water, and in an hour or two it is all over; the dry washes run with water, the thirsty land soaks up the water, and the bush creatures move out from under the trees where they have taken shelter with their rumps to the wind. The sun shines more strongly than ever, without the clouds of dust and the smoke from thousands of acres of burning grassland, and if you are trapped by a rising river, you need only wait an hour or two and then pass through a nearly empty bed.

In several weeks the grass is knee high, and in a couple of months the tallest grass is eight to ten feet high, although this is not general over the entire bush. In grass-less areas, such as near waterholes and on well-worn game trails, or on such car-tracks as exist, the mud gets deeper and deeper. The soil is sticky with clay or black mud, which is cloying and adhesive and almost rubbery to drive through. In fact, this type of soil, during the rains, is one of the few things through which even the Land Rover cannot consistently pass. If it should chance that two or three days go by without rain, the top of the soil will dry enough to give some traction, enough at least to give the optimist an excuse for driving through, but usually even then to his dismay.

The animals roam more freely now. You cannot always tell where the elephants will be, for instance, because they do not need to come back to the same waterhole each night. The zebra and wildebeeste leave the edges of the swamps and rivers and permanent lakes, and some-times migrate for hundreds of miles. The most classic example of this is the annual migration across the Serengeti Plain of hundreds of thousands of zebra and wildebeeste, which we were privileged to see. The leopard leaves the edges of the swamp where the game has congregated and will be found over a wider range. Eland, scarce in some areas toward the end of the dry season, reappear again when the rains come.

As the weeks go by, the swamps enlarge to cover many times their dry-season size. The lakes fill up, some of them having been dry enough to drive across only weeks before. The waterfowl begin arriving, since the wet season here providentially coincides with the coming of the cold weather in Europe, Russia, and other countries to the north. The spur-wing geese, plentiful even in the dry weather, proliferate into flocks of hundreds. The big beautiful Egyptian geese, arriving in small flocks, stay separate for the most part from the spurwings. Ducks and both black and white ibises cruise the bush and swamps in countless thousands.

Away from the edges of the swamp, deeper in the bush, you see the migrating flocks of tiny yellow flycatchers, and you are surprised to see swallows looking for all the world like the barn-swallows from home, and they may be similar, since I presume they also have come down from Europe to escape the winter.

So, this too, is the bush. Big. Green. Wet. Muddy. Pulsating with life.

This bush means many things to many people. To the farmer it is a wild country which must be cleared by hard, hot, back-breaking work. The bushes must be cut or burned. The thorn trees must be cut down, mindful of the two and three inch spikes. So to the farmer, the bush is the enemy. Many of the city-dwelling Africans, white and black, hate the bush. The bushman, primitive as stone-age man, lives in it. The tourist marvels at it, its great expanses, its vastness. The poacher, taking illegal elephant tusks, rhino horns, giraffe tails, ostrich feathers, crocodile skins, and any animal for its meat, lives off the bush. The conservationist, watching the dwindling bush, cries out to save it.

And the hunter—he hunts the bush:

One afternoon at four o'clock, Edna and Eric and I started out for a particularly wild area of bush called Chem Chem, which is a Swahili word meaning "spring." The bush and rolling hills and flat plains and high mountainous ridges of Chem Chem are one of the sources of the Great Sibiti River, running off to the northeast to Lake Eyasi. The other source is the Wembere River, running into and through Lake Kitangiri (or Lake Tulya as we usually call it), joining the rivers draining Chem Chem near Endasiku, a cluster of flat-topped mud houses fifty miles from nowhere, and very close to the land of the Wakindiga.

We went over the escarpment and dropped onto the Kidaru plains twelve hundred feet below. Then across Kidaru and the new settlements being hacked out of the bush (once prime hunting country in our own short time here), across five wide dry rivers, through the village of Kibaga where one can buy lukewarm Coca-cola from a tiny African shop, through the even smaller settlement which has grown up around the Catholic mission and is called for its sprawling neighbor—Chem Chem.

It was six PM when we passed through the Catholic mission and darkness was an hour away. The kwale ran in front of the car and flushed like partridge into the darkening bush. Tsetse flies buzzed around our heads. Zebra were startled from our path as we entered deeper and deeper into the uninhabited wilderness. Impala herds stampeded into the bush, then stood watching us carefully about a hundred yards away. We passed the dead

76

tree on which two vultures usually sit and noted that to-night they were absent from their perch. The track was easy to follow—two hard-worn wheel-paths, now climbing low hills, now dipping through dry washes. Two eland cows crashed away into the thorn trees and I looked for the bull to follow but never saw him. Two ostriches ran like cross-country racers, knees high, with gracefully long strides, trying to cut across in front of us. Three tiny Thomson's gazelles sprinted directly in front of the car, running low to the ground, ears back, terrified. We wondered at their presence so far (two miles at least) from their beloved open plains where they trust to vision and speed for safety.

The sun was on the horizon, blood-red and dropping fast, when we left the track to head for a small flat grassy swale in which I planned to camp. We came out of the bush at the southern end of the small plain and looked out on a grassy meadow about one half by one mile in area. Almost right in the middle were a dozen Tommies and one large red animal with a horse-like head and peculiar short curved horns standing on the back of the head—a hartebeeste, or better known locally as kongoni, a much more musical name for so beautiful an animal. As we drove out into the grass, I fully expected them all to race away, but only the Tommies ran, leaving the kongoni standing mesmerized while we drove up to within a hundred fifty yards, then a hundred twenty-five yards, then finally he began to trot slowly away, only to stop again at under a hundred fifty yards. We had come to hunt and here was one of the most desired animals in the African bush. I dropped him with my 30.06, and while Edna was fixing supper, Eric and I field-dressed him and propped him belly-down.

As the darkness of the bush dropped around us, we started a campfire with dried thorns for kindling and dried acacia limbs for the main fire. I wished that Sigurd F. Olson, who wrote so beautifully of the Quetico-Superior forest in *The Singing Wilderness* and *Listening Point,* could have been there with us so that he could write with his magic pen of what we saw and felt. The wind blew softly over the darkened bush, down onto our little island of yellow grass. The fire crackled brightly. I lay with my head on a rolled up sleeping bag, with Eric sitting contentedly close to the fire, tending it lovingly as only a small boy can. Edna sat a few feet away, watching the flames take hold of the dry wood, and wondering out loud how many pairs of eyes were watching us from the bush. At eight o'clock we began to watch the east, and soon we saw what we had really come for. It showed itself first as a faint lightening of the sky, with some trees silhouetting themselves on the nearest ridge. Then in a few more moments, the first gold of the full moon showed itself, and as we watched bewitched the entire orb climbed so fast we could see it move until it hung there, with the man in it laughing out loud. Gradually, the meadow and surrounding bush could be seen again, and within an hour it was so bright we could have seen a lion stalking her prey a hundred yards away. The crickets sang and the night wind rustled the long grass, and we felt the contentment of primitive man as he crouched by his little fire in the bush of Chem Chem, century upon century, and as the bushmen were doing this very night on the hills of Kindira only a few miles away.

Gone are the wars and rumors of wars. Far away are the flimsy constructions of steel and glass and concrete of puny man. Lost are the petty jealousies and hates and lusts of sinful man. Destroyed are the fears and terrors and lonely nights of the haunted city. Washed away by the light of the hunter's moon are the cares and troubles of mortal man. Here is the wide sweep of plain and forest. Here is the nightbird and prowling predator. Here is the wind and the sky and the grass. Here in this place is peace. Take off your shoes, for where you stand is holy ground. For here, in this bush, is God.

7

THE HUNT—WEDNESDAY

7:00: Alpha at Iambi, three hours away by Land Rover, insists over the radio that I have just got to get over there to see some patients for her. I tell her I just can't get away this week, as busy as we are and with Joe gone. She is unhappy.

7:15: I gulp two chloroquin tablets, prophylaxis against malaria, and congratulate myself on maneuvering them down without tasting their bitterness. Ten years ago in Korea we took one tablet once a week. Here we take two tablets twice a week, and no one can tell me the reason for the change. Presumably there were too many cases of malaria even on prophylaxis, although I can't recall any cases in my batallion.

8:30: Breakfast, then vespers as usual. Rounds go quickly this morning. There have been a few new admissions, and we spend a few extra minutes with them. The postoperative patients are all in satisfactory condition.

9:30: Fred Malloy comes down to see if I can go hunting. I tell him that possibly about 11:00 or 11:30 I could get away. We finish rounds.

11:00: Dick and I go up to the house, hoping to get away for the rest of the day. But no sooner have I gotten

Mtaturu young man
from Wembere Plains.
His walking bank
account (cows) is worth
10,000 shillings
(about $1,400)

Baobab tree in the dry season, looking as if ripped up by the
devil and pushed back into the ground upside down

Giraffe, in Tsavo
National Game Reserve

Zebra, in Ngorongoro Crater

Welu Nzao, a typical Iramba lady, who works at the hospital as a midwife

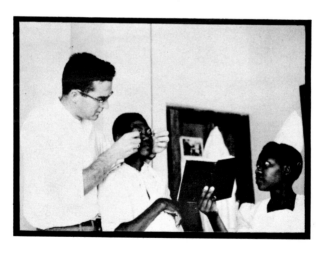

Dr. Joe Norquist fitting lenses to postoperative cataract patient, Kiomboi Hospital

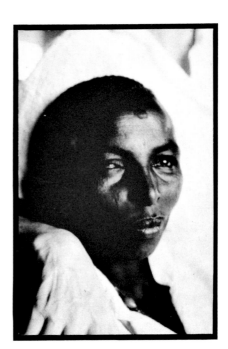

Woman who lived in
the bush alone for
fourteen years, until
found by Louise Faust

Barabaig men

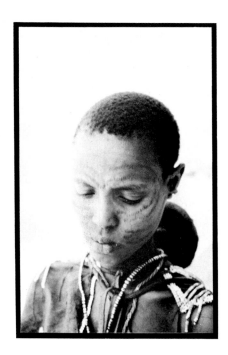

Barabaig woman

Young Wakindiga women, who have discarded clothes of skins in favor of "shukas."

Author examining Wakindiga people

Medical Assistant
Sampson Paulo
(see dedication)

Iramba women waiting for examination outside Ward E, gynecology, Kiomboi

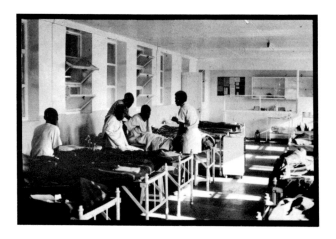

Ward A, men's surgical ward, Kiomboi

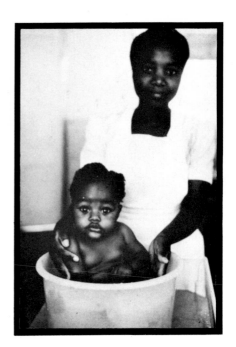

Student nurse bathing
baby on Ward B,
Kiomboi Hospital

Miaombo, Mkindiga young man, making poison arrows

out of hospital whites into hunting browns than I am called back to see some Indian outpatients. I think at first that they must be the ones I put off yesterday, but find it to be an old friend of mine, Hassam H. Devji, a chronic cardiac always full of the multiple complaints of old age for which I can do nothing. Sometimes he comes in in mild heart failure, with a little fluid in his lungs, and needs an injection to help move the water. This is the case today, and after offering my condolences for his other problems, I am able to get away.

12:00 noon: Fred picks us up in his beat-up old green jeep truck. Eric goes along, since school is out, and nearly bursts with enthusiasm. He rides in the back with an African worker from the school whom Fred has brought along to help with the game. We head down the Singida road, almost to Ulemo, then turn off to the south on the Ushora road. It is in the process of being improved from a bumpy car-track into a wider, flatter, dry-weather road. For about five miles we slush through recently graded sandy loam, then come to the road-workers themselves. From there on, the road consists of two wheel tracks deep into nearly uninhabited bush. We pass Mr. Stainer's well-digging rig, and his wife and teen-age daughter wave to us from their trailer. We drive over to say hello. They have just moved in a few days ago, and haven't seen any eland. They direct us to the African workers' camp, where we pick up a "guide," a scrawny old man clothed in a worn-out, mustard-colored English Army overcoat. I have had experience with these apparent derelicts. They are the true eyes of the white man and can spot and differentiate game at incredible distances. On one occasion, our scout spotted an old black-maned lion on a hillside some distance away; I couldn't see it. We drove nearly half the distance to the animal before I could spot it, and my eyes are better than 20/20. So since it is not

81

the visual acuity per se, it must be that these scouts can see breaks in the grass and bush patterns which cannot be explained other than by the presence of an animal, and the general shape and color of the "break" gives them a clue as to the identity of the animal.

A further reason for taking a guide is the vastness and tracklessness of most good hunting country. A native of the area recognizes landmarks which are really not landmarks to the infrequent visitor. He has points of reference which he may have difficulty explaining to anyone, but which guide him across a flat plain or through dense bush. And when you have turned and twisted and backtracked and gone in circles all day without a thought to where you are, you say to the guide, "Let's go home," and the guide points in the direction of camp or of the track, and out you go. Sometimes it is unbelievable how he can pinpoint a camp and lead you right to it.

A third reason for taking a guide is to track wounded game. Most hunting is done in the dry season with the ground nearly as hard as rock, and it takes almost uncanny tracking ability to follow a lone animal across it. I lost one big, beautiful buck hartebeeste one day, hunting alone in Chem Chem, because I was unable to track him. We should use guides more often, I suppose, but usually we hunt in areas where we ourselves feel confident about our knowledge of the bush, and consequently we go without one. Today, Fred feels we should have someone with us.

1:30: So we go off with Msengi into some of the roughest-riding country in our area. The ground is broken by closely clustered tufts of grass growing in small hillocks about six inches high, resembling a dry bog more than anything. We jar along for about two miles through good brushy impala country, out into a wide open plain broken by scattered patches of thorn trees. It is hot, and dusty as well. We realize right away that we will be lucky indeed to see any eland until later in the day.

3:00: We spot a herd of about fifteen zebra. Fred is itching to try out his new .375 magnum. We drop off the side and walk slowly toward the herd. They are all watching intently at about five hundred yards. Too far for even the best shot. We walk them up slowly. Three-fifty. Three hundred. They continue to watch. None are grazing now. Two-fifty. One breaks nervously and trots around the herd, beautiful muscles rippling black and white in the shimmering sun. Another one trots off into the bush, then comes back to stand and eye us. This is not a frequently hunted area, or these animals would have been gone long ago. Either that or we would have had to do a formal stalk on hands and knees to get this close.

(Let me dispel a common myth. One does not just walk up to a zebra and shoot it. The zebra ranks with the most difficult of animals to get close enough to to get in a good shot. I well remember a magazine article which depicted a young boy shooting at a zebra at an impossibly close distance, and killing it with one shot from a small bore rifle. I have this to say about that: Somehow that hunt was faked, because it is impossible to get that close to a wild zebra outside of a protected area, unless by a long hands-and-knees stalk by a careful, experienced hunter.)

At two hundred twenty-five yards, Fred decides he is going to lose the herd, or he is going to have to stalk them on hands and knees, and he doesn't feel like doing either. He braces against a tree, starts the squeeze, and lets up. The whole herd has broken into a slow trot, at an angle of about forty-five degrees from our line of approach. We follow them for a couple hundred yards, when they stop and watch us again. They are now about two hundred fifty yards out. Even in the telescope they look pretty small for a clean kill. Stories of clean kills at four hundred and even five hundred yards may be true, but my own opinion of that type of shooting should not be printed here.

3:45: Fred wants a skin. We move very slowly up on the now wary animals, in a half crouch, staying behind bushes as much as possible. Fred says, "About two hundred yards now, doc?"

"Yeah, Fred, little more maybe."

"I'm gonna try 'er."

"Go ahead. I'll line up, too, if you'd like."

"Yeah, do that."

We brace on thorn trees, and Fred pulls down slowly. Crack! Thuuwwuump! The whole herd is gone except one. He stands for a moment, dazed, then trots off, too, picking up speed as he goes. I am so sure he is going to go down that I don't even shoot.

Fred glances at me, "Why didn't you shoot?"

"Thought you had him, Fred!"

"These are zebra, doc. They don't often go down with one shot."

"I know, Fred." Guiltily.

We follow for better than an hour, at first by sight, then by tracks, finally losing them altogether.

5:00: We're both disgusted. We've spent two hours on nothing. We find the truck with a little trouble, then push on.

5:05: "Pofu, bwana, pofu," Msengi whispers excitedly. And there they are—about thirty eland grazing on the edge of a meadow. One giant bull, almost black with age and virility, stands with head up, watching us approach. We are still five hundred to six hundred yards away. He looks like he'd be about 1,800 pounds on the hoof. He's about twice the size of the smaller cows nearby. What a lordly creature, with straight massive horns with a spiral groove twisting around each horn. We can't get anywhere near them. Off they go in a cloud of dust, disappearing into the bush like mice in a wheat field.

"I'll bet that bull goes a ton, doc," Fred says.

"They don't get that big, Fred," I answer, "except like a fish that gets longer with each telling."

Fred grunts. Fred is a typical sportsman. That eland weighs a ton! That elephant was only twenty feet from me! You should have seen the game here last year! I had two or three hundred tsetse fly bites all over me! Ad infinitum. It makes me mad. I can't ever top him, and I'm pretty good myself in this department, like catching seven pound smallmouths every time I float the Red Cedar!

5:25: We bounce slowly on, swinging in a wide arc which will bring us back to the track we followed in. We spot another small herd of eland, this time about four hundred yards away and with a half acre of dense thornbush alongside them. We circle the thornbush at a respectful distance, and fortunately the wind is coming directly in our faces as Fred and I make our way on foot through the bush. Suddenly, I am startled out of my khakis by a yellow and black form that flushes out from the tall yellow grass just twenty-five yards ahead of me. It takes just an instant to recognize it as a small leopard. While I am trying to decide whether or not to shoot it, it disappears into the bush. I begin to wish then that I had shot, since leopard skins are not easy to come by.

Fred is about fifty yards away. He has seen my "friend" streaking out ahead. He grins, and indicates in sign language that I should have shot. I indicate unmistakably that I was too scared!

5:40: We go into a slow crouching stalk, manage to traverse the bush clear to the other edge, and are greeted by a thoroughly breathtaking sight. We both stop involuntarily just to look. About a hundred fifty yards away is a scattered herd of zebra, mostly with heads up, watching in our direction, suspecting, but not seeing or smelling anything dangerous. Off to both sides of the zebra are three small herds of eland, the closest perhaps a hundred seventy-five to two hundred yards away. Behind them are four giraffe, the only animals who have spotted us. They stand stiff and straight, ready for flight, and if they go, all the animals will go. I hear Fred mumbling under his breath, and know he's pleading with those giraffe to hold up. Behind those beautiful animals stretch the long, wide yellow-green plains, and painted against the dusty yellow-blue sky is the setting sun. It is a sight to remember all my life.

5:50: Fred and I exchange looks. It's now or never. Slowly Fred points to himself and then to the herd of eland to his left. I understand and indicate I will try to my right, to make sure we're not shooting at the same animal. I watch Fred cautiously slide the barrel of his .375 into position, and slide my own 30.06 into a crotch of a tree. I pick out a bull that looks the closest and that, at the same time, is broadside. Fred takes a long time. The zebra are getting nervous, and one of the giraffes has started to walk slowly away. I'm holding down tight on my animal, and as I hear the crack of Fred's gun I fire also. One animal goes down. Mine. Fred hollers, "I must have missed." I'm already on the run, trying to get as close as possible for a second shot if the animal gets up. Out of the corner of my eye I see one of the most beautiful spectacles in all the world: eland, zebra, and giraffe in full flight across the plains, with clouds of dust billowing into the windy dusk. The zebra disappear into the bush a mile away, but the eland stop about a quarter of a mile away. One of them is in trouble, and as I watch, he falls over and lies still. The four giraffe stand in a semi-circle.

6:00: We walk over to Fred's eland. A medium-sized animal, possibly around eight hundred to nine hundred pounds. We hear the truck crashing through the brush behind us, our party having been instructed to come up when they heard shots. Eric is beaming as only an eight-year-old can. The two Africans are all business, and soon knives are working. It will be dark before long and trackless plain is hard to get out of after dark.

6:10: We load up Fred's eland and go over after mine. I haven't told Eric that I got one, too, and when he spots the other animal in the grass he does a good old-fashioned double take and nearly jumps out of the truck. His eyes light up, and his face breaks out into a grin that melts the cockles of this old white hunter's heart. He is so ingenuously and innocently proud of his Dad. We load up the other animal.

6:20: Fred turns to Msengi without a word. Msengi points, also without a word. In about forty-five minutes we come upon the track, sidling in at about a ten degree angle. In this bush, fifty yards off in either direction would have been too much, and we would have missed the track. It is now almost dark.

7:15: We leave Msengi off at his camp and tell him to cut a haunch off one of the eland. He is greatly pleased, since he already has unloaded the liver and intestines which would have satisfied him for payment for his guide services.

8:15: We arrive at home without further difficulty. There is a message for me to see a baby with a possible intussusception. I change clothes hurriedly and go down to Ward B. I go over the history with the mother and examine the child. From the history, I am strongly suspicious, but the physical examination shows me nothing to be concerned about. To be on the safe side, however,

I order a tube to be passed into the stomach and fluids to be started by cutdown.

8:55: Fred and I discuss the recent labor problems over a sandwich and a cup of coffee at our house. Fred has very strong opinions on the utilization of local labor. He thinks the Africans should be (a) taught well, on the job if necessary; (b) made to work well by constant supervision; and then (c) paid well. With this philosophy he gets along well with both the workers and with the local union officers. During Fred's absence during the past year, Tanganyika won its independence, and workers and union leaders began to make extremely unreasonable demands, quoting nonexistent laws, calling extemporaneous workers' meetings, and in general making a great deal of trouble for us at the hospital. Fred's steady hand and personal attention to his three principles have improved the situation.

10:30: It has been a long hard exciting day, with three hours' sleep last night. I go to bed before the lights go out, thinking briefly of the little baby with the possible bowel obstruction and having that familiar uneasy feeling that I get when I'm "sitting on" a case waiting for certain signs or symptoms to develop to cinch the diagnosis.

8

CHICKEN LIVERS, DICED
PLACENTAE, AND CASTOR BEANS

As I have mentioned before, the Iramba tribe is a considerably enlightened tribe when compared to the half-dozen tribes surrounding it. The reasons for this are several and include (not necessarily in order of importance): (a) accessibility (roads, railroad), (b) occupation of the majority (farming), (c) early attempts by British colonialists to educate the tribe, (d) mission activity over an even longer period of time, (e) malleableness of the tribal culture patterns to accept education. There may be other reasons which could be enumerated by a more careful study of the problem, but these are the main ones as I see it.

In consequence of this relatively high level of education, one might expect a rather enlightened view of disease, medical practices, and the medical practitioners. And possibly, taken in context of the *average* African's understanding of disease, it may be on a higher level, but I think it might be interesting to look at some of the modern-day Iramba's thinking.

General Attitudes

The general attitudes of the Iramba people toward American (or European) medicine are gradually changing, it is true, but many of the old beliefs and superstitions linger, especially in the older people. The people no longer believe that the American doctor heals oftener merely because his "magic" is stronger. They believe rather that the American doctors and nurses have lot of "akili" (a Swahili word which may be translated variably as ability, cleverness, common sense, or intelligence). But, being used to the pseudo-scientists who are more likely to promise more than the true scientist, the cuckolded husband can ask seriously, "Please examine my pregnant wife and tell me the exact date she conceived and name the father of the child."

Despite this incredible naïvete and blind faith in the "akili" of the American doctor, the average Iramba will still take the advice of his own medicine man if his pronouncements are at odds with those of the American doctor. How often this situation occurs and must be put to the test is obviously impossible to assess, but that it does happen is not doubted.

Other paradoxes occur. The hospital personnel have been doing surgery for thirty years and all cases are not successful. An occasional bad result is inevitable, and death does occur. Gradually the people have come to accept the fact that even the American doctors are incapable of curing everything, and that sometimes patients will die even after surgery. Years ago they might have blamed the doctor but now they understand things better and tend to blame themselves for not going to the hospital sooner.

Now, with this great faith and trust, you would expect that instructions would be followed to the letter. Not so. Patients practically never follow instructions in taking medicine at home. They stop taking their medicine too soon, even before they feel better. They may save it for another illness, or they may sell it to someone with (presumably) the same illness. However, they will seldom take the whole supply at once on the theory that if a little is good, a lot will be better.

Somehow the injection has become the symbol for a curative procedure. Margaret Peterson, a nurse at Kiomboi for twenty-five years, conjectures that it may be due to the nearly miraculous cures effected in yaws by Bismuth injections when she first came to Africa. Yaws has been completely eradicated, and the continued miracles wrought by penicillin in a host of diseases, including yaws, may be the cause for the favoring of the "sindano" over liquids or pills.

The use of the modern diagnostic instruments is not well understood. The people no longer think of them as having supernatural significance, but often consider that they have had a treatment if the doctor has listened to their chests with a stethoscope. X-rays are totally incomprehensible. This lack of understanding is not confined to Africa; I have had patients in the United States comment to me how much better they felt after their treatment, when actually they had had routine diagnostic pictures taken.

We do autopsies whenever possible and find the resistance on the part of the relatives to be about the same as in the United States, so our rate is about forty to fifty percent on in-hospital deaths. We also autopsy the rather frequent victims of suicide, murder, and death by violence in many forms. (This is one of our more distasteful tasks, since the bodies are usually several days old by the time we receive them.)

Tribal Doctors

There is a very clear-cut distinction between "medicine man" and "witch doctor." The medicine man (mganga) utilizes products of the trees and gardens to treat patients, whereas the witch doctor (mchawi) looks into the liver of a chicken and sees the reflection there of the one who might have brought the illness. Also, the witch doctor is never seen since he always goes in through the windows. He is called the "fici ya usiku," the hyena of the night. The medicine men, therefore, are trusted practitioners of medicine; the witch doctors are feared practitioners of sorcery and witchcraft.

The medicine men are taught by other members of the family, usually a father-to-son inheritance. An outsider is occasionally permitted to apprentice himself to a medicine man, but only at a very high price. The young men begin study in their youth and continue to learn until the father dies, at which time they take over completely.

Iramba medicine men do not specialize in the treatment of certain diseases, but a few women medical practitioners specialize in sterility problems; the men also treat this. Since the great majority of sterility problems are due to actual closure of the tubes from the scarring of gonorrheal infections, the successful cases must be few.

The medicine men are occasionally called in difficult obstetrical cases and will use medicines in treatment. They will also do manual extraction of the baby and/or placenta if they are far from the hospital.

It is obvious that some of the medicines used by the tribal doctors are potent. They often cause sloughing of the skin where they are applied, necessitating plastic surgery for restoration of skin. These cases range from the relatively simple grafting of skin onto flat surfaces to the complicated complete reconstruction of parts of the face. Another drug produces a clinical picture alarmingly similar to a bowel obstruction, and only by means of an agonizing wait can the two be distinguished. The drug cases get better; the bowel obstructions get worse and are then operated. In the United States, bowel obstructions display a rather characteristic set of symptoms and physical findings and usually are operated as emergencies. In Iramba-land, we have to sit tight to wait for the differentiation.

The medicine men in general do not take histories or do examinations. The patient comes saying, "I'm sick," and expects diagnosis and treatment. Usually a word or two to identify the symptom, and then the drug most likely to help is given right on the spot. In addition to drugs, "multiple scarification" is often done. This consists of multiple skin-deep incisions over a growing tumor or a painful joint. This is so commonplace that we rarely see a patient who does not have scars somewhere on his body from previous treatments. Patients with chronic diseases, such as asthma, arthritis, or slowly growing abdominal tumors, will have hundreds of scars on the affected parts.

Maternal and Obstetrical Beliefs and Practices

A great number of strange beliefs surround the mother as she approaches her day of delivery. We would laugh and call these attitudes "superstitions," but to the African mother-to-be, it is no laughing matter. If she has been unknowingly bewitched, her child may be a Mongolian idiot, or have a tiny head (microcephaly), or any one of many other congenital defects. Fortunately, the more common aberrations, for example extra fingers or toes, are known to be inherited. Breech presentation merely means the child will be a "bad one"—unmanageable—and as the child gets older, even this will be forgotten.

Some Irambas feel that some birth defects, such as absence of an extremity, are due to the will of God (or plan, or order, of God—"Shauri la Mungu"). There is, in fact, some vagueness in this area, and this merely compounds the fears which the mother faces.

Twins are welcome, and there is much joy when they arrive. A lamb is killed even before the cords are cut, and this sets off a general celebration. If lightning occurs while the women are still with the mother, those women will also be likely to have twins. The placenta (after-birth) of the twins is taken out and dried over a fire, then carried to the river in a hollow gourd on the shoulder instead of the customary position on the head, and covered with a large amount of dry sand. This will help to bring rains in their season. An alternate method of disposal is to put tiny pieces of the placenta with the grain seeds in order to insure a good harvest. Or small pieces may be given to the goats in order that they give birth. The magic of the double birth, the power of the fertility of this woman, is then preserved in as many ways as possible—to bring rains, to grow grain, to produce livestock. We, the emancipated, laugh, but they, the entrapped, do not understand our laughter, for to them this is real and right.

The placenta of a single birth is not handled with such elaborateness, but is merely placed in a freshly dug hole at arm's length and the hole carefully packed with dirt. It certainly must not be carelessly thrown away, or the woman will not bear again. This custom does cause an occasional problem at the hospital since it is not thought wise to either overtly deride this superstition or to give it credence by acceding to the mother's wishes. Each time, Welu Nzao or Anna Enoki is able to convince the mother by telling her that three generations of women have delivered here even after the hospital has disposed of the placenta.

No figures are available as to the number of women who die in childbirth out in the bush. Certainly a large number of those who get into trouble are brought to Kiomboi.

The case described in the chapter "The Hospital—Monday" is not uncommon, and the timing is almost always the same, usually about three days. During the first day, no one is worried. During the second day, the medicine man may have his opportunity to give the correct herbs to accomplish delivery. During the third day, the relatives are concerned that the mother may have been bewitched, and the witch doctor is called to look into a chicken's liver to see who is responsible. By the end of the third day, it becomes obvious that the witch-doctor has not succeeded. If illegitimacy is known or suspected and the culprit is known, he will be made to urinate into an animal's horn pushed through the wall of the mudhouse and the laboring mother forced to drink a little of the urine. If this doesn't produce results, someone may now suggest taking the woman to the white man's hospital. Even this last resort fails occasionally, the baby being dead already, or dying. And sometimes the mother dies and the baby lives, and the grandmother and father sorrowfully carry the tiny newborn home to a motherless hut, there to die of malnutrition unless a wet nurse can be opportunely found. If the mother was unmarried and the father known, he will be fined by the native courts the amount he would have paid the woman's father to obtain her in marriage.

Sterility is the curse brought by gonorrhea. Gonorrhea is almost universal in the hospital-patient population, and therefore must be similarly widespread outside the hospital. Many erroneous beliefs are widespread concerning sterility, and one of the most amusing (to us) is the method still used to determine which of the married partners is the sterile one. Castor beans are collected, and their oil is put into two pots over two fires, one for the man and one for the woman. The oil which burns first represents the one with the fertile "seed," and the rest of the oil is placed in the rectum (like an enema) of the one who is now judged to be the sterile partner. It is interesting to note that this tribe recognizes that the male may be sterile, a fact just now receiving reluctant credibility in the United States.

Concerning gonorrhea itself, only the educated younger generation realizes that the disease is contagious, and only they recognize it as a cause of sterility. The rest have somehow failed to detect the cause-effect relationship.

Attitudes Concerning Some Specific Illnesses

I have mentioned a few specific diseases in this chapter as we have gone along. Many others remain, and the Irambas have some interesting ideas about their causes.

It almost goes without saying that mental illnesses, epilepsy, meningitis, and other forms of brain disease would be considered due to witchcraft. The general belief is that when a person develops one of these illnesses, someone else has gone to a witch doctor to get medicine to bewitch the sick one. If the person recovers, the bewitchment failed, but the now-recovered person will never be given any position of responsibility in the village, such as headman.

Leprosy is one of the few diseases, maybe the only one, which is recognized by nearly everyone as being contagious. Even here, however, some believe that the leprous person has stolen from someone and now has been punished. In general, the Iramba people believe that the disease can be transmitted from person to person, and may follow in successive generations in a family. Divorce is permitted if the spouse contracts leprosy, but usually is not obtained because the nonleprous spouse recognizes that he (she) may get the disease and then would have trouble finding another marriage partner. If the leprous one has the severely contagious form of the disease and is sent to the leprosarium (for a minimum of two years, usually longer), the nonleprous one will often move there with him (her). If the leprous one can be treated as an outpatient, the nonleprous one will just sleep in a different bed while the leprous one is receiving treatment. (Much, much more could be written about leprosy itself and the interesting and sometimes tragic socioeconomic problems which it produces.)

Tuberculosis and smallpox, though dissimilar in manifestations, are thought by the Irambas to be caused by a somewhat different type of witchcraft—a depersonalized form, if you will. These diseases are gotten when someone has thrown a witch doctor's medicine in the air, maybe in hopes that the specific target-person will be contaminated, or maybe in a blind striking-out at a large group of persons. A point of interest is that these two diseases are recognized as being caught "through the air," which in fact is true in nearly every case.

"Snail fever" [urinary (bilharzia) and intestinal schistosomiasis] is not linked to contaminated water at all, but rather is "known" to have been brought by the early European visitors. (Some think that venereal disease came this way also.) This disease is one of our major problems and at the present time can only be controlled by education and by treating the cases as they arise. In one highly endemic area ten miles from Kiomboi, we have convinced the headman, Yakobo Ntundu, that there *is* a relationship between the water supply and the many cases of bloody urine, and in his village-area new wells are being dug even now.

Malaria, involving nearly a hundred percent of the population and responsible for much of the infant mortality, is thought to be due to witchcraft, the enemies of the night. No native medicines have specific anti-malarial properties, so the people can only treat themselves in the usual manner—finding the bewitcher from the witch doctor's chicken livers.

Albinos, seen frequently in our part of East Africa, used to be drowned, but now are accepted. A peculiar-looking condition, it is very troublesome to the afflicted ones since they must markedly limit their exposure to the sun for fear of burning. In equatorial Africa, this is difficult.

Even after this review of but a small part of the beliefs that the "average" Iramba entertains, you will recognize the complex intermingling of the old superstitions with the new concepts which are being introduced. The ancient framework is still there and oftentimes the new ideas do not even supplant the old ones, but merely take their place in the thought structure of the individual. For example, I was asked in all seriousness by a young *student nurse* to cure her medical problem by finding out the person who had bewitched her! Temporarily forgotten because of its relative insignificance within the total context of my experience, this incident is now recalled and received by my own mind with some incredulity. Yet it happened.

So the African, even if educated, lives in a world populated by unknown elements and unseen, nether-worldly shades. The following account didn't actually happen— but it could have:

9

THE DOCTOR LAUGHED

I should have known right away what had happened to me. My roots deep in the sandy soil of eroded highlands, my whole being attuned to the chants of the medicine men, my heart pulled back into the animism of centuries of my black forefathers, my very head scarred from the red-hot coals my mother forced there to prevent my good spirits from leaving through the fontannel of my babyhood. All these and many more. And still I did not awaken to the reality of my own torment until it was already too late. Or did I just not want to?

My brain throbbed in its unyielding skull, and fireflies danced through the blood-red light that filled my pupils. The narrow path through the shoulder-high millet fields wound in tortuously tight circles, or so it seemed, and the hospital grew ever farther away. But now that I knew what was wrong, maybe it mattered little if I ever reached it. I lay down on the hot dusty ground by the side of the path to think.

How had it happened? Only two days ago I had been nearly beside myself with happiness. My father's house of crumbling mud-brick had reverberated with the sound of singing and dancing, and my older brother and two younger sisters congratulated me on my acceptance to secondary school. Even my father, who would probably have to sell a good cow to pay the first tuition fees, had a half-shy, half-disturbed smile on his lips. For it was good to have a son go on to higher schooling. Even now, it was already commonplace to have a son with a standard-four education, and there were too many of the village elders who could boast of their sons with standard-eight educations who were clerks at the government offices; and even the young girls were learning to speak English, using their new-found language to talk secretly in front of their elders!

So I revelled in my success and accepted gracefully the accolades of my less-fortunate contemporaries. We sat on the mud floor and on small stools and munched un-roasted peanuts and roasted corn from my mother's fields. There was only one incident to mar the otherwise happy festivities.

I sat contentedly in the warm glow of friendship, staring out the low doorway at the silhouette of the giant baobab tree which was the home of our village's own benevolent spirit. Contemplating this tree alone should have been enough to prevent what happened next.

Quite suddenly, I felt that unexplainable urge to turn my head, and doing so, was caught by the black eyes in the black face of one of my sister's friends. Her face was a mask, with no emotion save hate, her black shuka drawn low over her forehead and wrapped around her shoulders and body as a shroud. Her eyes flashed, and I could not tear my own away. We locked in that horrible intercourse for an indeterminate time, and my thoughts stood still. Her mouth worked, and she whispered something I could not hear. Then the ugly face relaxed, the eyes once black with venom now danced with the light from the setting sun coming in the door, and throwing her shuka back from her face, she jumped up laughing and joined my sister and her friends. The entire episode might never have happened. Indeed, for two days now I had forgotten it.

As I lay prostrate in the sun, I once again saw that evil face and those darkening eyes. I rolled over on my back and could feel the dry grass and coarse sand rustle under my head. The sky was dark blue, no rain clouds now to mar its uniformity, the rainy season now abating. Two black and white crows sailed screeching across the arc. A lonely vulture wheeled high, guarding his own well-marked territory in space, watching, watching, and if seeing, descending; and seeing him descend, another vulture leaving his post, following, descending; and then another, and another, each marking time in lonely orbit until the sharpened eye sees the neighbors go down to the carrion-feast. Is this my fate? Seeing that black-shrouded face and hate-riven eyes, I know that it is true. For I have been bewitched!

I know why, too.

Many years ago my boyhood haunts included the same rolling hills and the same thorn thickets and the same millet fields that I now call home. For my father is a farmer, as are all my relatives. He, and his father, and his father's father tilled these same sandy hills. We learned in school that sometime in the not-too-distant past our forefathers moved in to escape the encroachment of more warlike tribes in the north, but no one now alive can remember that. Herding goats and cattle fell to my lot when I was old enough to carry a knob-ended throwing stick. Unlike my Barabaig and Sukuma neighbors, however, I didn't carry a spear, since our area was not threatened so constantly by lion and leopard. When I was eight, my father told me I was chosen to begin primary school. For several weeks I was alternately elated and

101

frightened, and during my more depressed moods I would gladly have traded my future to one of my older brothers, who had been bypassed in my favor because they were too old to begin school.

But once in school, I found it to my liking and moved rapidly ahead in my learning.

When I was ten, an incident occurred which has now reached forward into time to shape my life, or rather my death. It started innocently enough. My two brothers, my youngest sister, and her friend (the one in the black shuka), and I went one day down to a wide bend in the Zalala River to bathe and swim. It was a hot day, and a heavy rain during the night had raised the river level to a dangerous height. Kiula, my oldest brother, and Tatu, my sister's friend, tagged along in the rear. He was about fifteen, she twelve, and they were much taken with each other, but hardly dared show it because that would not have been correct conduct in our tribe at that age. It was a beautiful day, full of no ominous portents, and we laughed and played in the water. At last the two girls tired, climbed out onto the bank, and sat drying in the sun. Mpingu, my other brother, left for home, while Kiula and I continued to swim. Finally we also tired, and climbed out, I leading the way up the steep bank. Suddenly the sand gave way under Kiula's feet, and he plunged down the bank toward the deepest part of the pool. I made a desperate lunge after him, missed, and sprawled face down at the shallow edge of the water, from where I was able to scramble back to safety. Not so Kiula. His head hit a rock and he sank from sight immediately. By the time I found him in the muddy water, he was dead.

I looked up at my sister and Tatu. Tatu looked at me with fear, disgust, and hate. I started under her gaze.

"Why do you look at me thus?" I said.

"You pushed him," she answered.

"I pushed him? No, it is not true. I tried to catch him when he slipped."

"You lie. I saw you. You pushed him."

She would not listen to me. My sister looked quickly from her face to mine, trying to judge who was right. She clearly did not know what had happened.

"Tell her, sister," I said. "Tell her I could not do such a thing!"

She sided with me, and for several moments they argued with vehemence. Finally Tatu said to me, "Some day your turn shall come. You will see. You also will die before your time."

I hung my head. Was it not bad enough that Kiula was dead? Must I also be accused falsely of causing his death? This was more than I could bear. I ran to our house and threw myself down on the mat in the far corner of the room, leaving the girls to call men to bring back Kiula's body.

In the days that followed, Tatu continued to come to the house and my sister's acceptance of her convinced me that they both now felt I was guilty. But apparently my sister's will won out in the end, and I was never accused by any other man, though I could never meet the eyes of Tatu again.

Not until two days ago. For six years we had not exchanged a look or a word. I was away at school for long periods of time and preferred to ignore rumors that Tatu was spending an inordinate number of hours with the witch doctor who lived in the village close by ours.

Now as I lay watching the vulture soaring above me, all this came back to me. Slowly I pulled myself to my feet, every muscle aching, my eyes staring out of their sunken sockets, my head pounding with black blood. I must find the witch doctor. I will turn back from this path that leads to the white man's hospital. He would not understand. He would laugh. Besides, he can do nothing against this evil curse.

I glanced dazedly around me. Which way should I go? Discerning the giant baobab through my misting eyes, I struggled toward it, thinking I could begin my search from there. I never reached it.

Through a black haze, I felt the bouncing of the wood and wicker bed under me and heard the matching tread of four pairs of naked feet shuffling in the dust as they bore me through the night. Do they think I am dead? Are they carrying me to my grave? I tried to cry out, but could not. A wave of nausea overcame me, and I sank down deeper into semiconsciousness. If I could vomit, then they'd know I'm alive.

A blinding light glared through my closed lids. Voices talking in English and in Swahili. Darkness again. Then a more subdued light. Two Americans talking: "They found him in the mitama shamba, stretched out cold. Look at his belly. Looks like a bowel obstruction." Good, at least they know I'm not dead. But what can they do, when I've been bewitched?

The American doctors again asking questions. Vomiting? Yes. Previous surgery? Let's have a look at his belly again. No, no scars. Diarrhea? We don't know. How long has he been sick? Only a few hours.

A warm hand on my wrist. A cold round object on my chest, then my belly. Probing, searching fingers, deep in my belly. Is it possible their magic is greater than Tatu's? It might be so.

I feel a sharp sting in front of my elbow, a needle sliding in, a burning sensation running up the inside of my arm.

"Don't run that too fast. Wait till we get a baseline on his pressure, and a count on the rate of flow."

Gibberish. What were they saying? I learned English and I don't recognize any of that. Part of the magic? I begin to believe that maybe they have some power over evil after all. I open my eyes. I say in Swahili, "I have been bewitched."

The younger doctor looks at the older. "What does he mean, nimelogwa."

"He says he has been bewitched."

"Bewitched? Ha, that's a good one."

The spell, counteracting the spell, is shattered. They don't believe. I feel myself sinking again. Nausea, and a sudden gush of vomit fills my mouth and overflows on the bed. I take a deep breath, and the vomit fills my lungs. The black eyes in the black face under the black shuka burn into my brain. The fires dance, and fall, and dance again. And the witches from the other world join hands with the black-eyed witch and carry me down, down, down. . . .

10

THE HOSPITAL—THURSDAY

7:00: I wake up with an uneasy feeling, and for a moment can't identify the reason. The baby! They haven't called me all night, so it must be all right. But I have had these funny premonitions before, and I am worried.

7:10: The light plant hasn't come on yet, so I dress and shave while waiting for it to go on to power the radio. When it fails to come on this morning, we miss radio completely.

7:45: I hurry to the hospital, telling myself I could have slowed breakfast down a little, since if there was any trouble they surely would have called me.

7:50: As I round the corner in the main building, a student nurse comes running out of Ward B, catches sight of me, and calls urgently, "Come quickly, doctor!" I break into a run. It can mean only one thing. Why didn't I come down before breakfast?

7:52: The baby is dead. I can see the reason. There is vomitus on the face and in the bed. The nasogastric tube hangs impotently from the baby's nose, obviously not having functioned or the baby would still be alive. The baby has vomited and aspirated and choked to death. All within fifteen feet of the nurses' desk. I try to reconstruct the events and all I can find out is that the baby

106

slept well all night, suddenly awoke, cried out, vomited, aspirated, and died. I ask for permission to do a post-mortem examination, and the mother agrees. At least we will find out what the underlying disease is. The thought crosses my mind—what if there is an intussusception, a surgically correctable condition? Well, we will soon know, possibly to our discredit.

8:05: I go over to morning vespers, and am unable to understand the little girl leading the service because of her soft slurring speech with the singsong lilt of an Iramba accent.

8:25: I go over to our "morgue," an isolated six by ten foot cubbyhole attached to Ward B. I am stopped by David Msengi who informs me that the father of the baby has refused permission to have an autopsy done. We look for the father to try to dissuade him, but are unable to find him. Crying and moaning has started in the court-yard. This is not a Christian family and I suspect that a "death dance" is in the offing.

8:45: We start rounds. The patient who had the huge cancerous ovary is distended and very uncomfortable, but otherwise doing well. The girl who had a manual re-moval of the placenta is localizing an abscess and I am now sure she will have to be operated. The patient who had the pelvic tumor and spleen removed is very tender around the incision and has begun to run a temperature, but she looks good and feels good. The postop C-sections are fine. On Ward C, I send home several patients, and notice that three of the six patients with bilharzia are from the same village, Ulemo, and we must be on the alert for more from there, and go down there on a public health expedition if many more turn up. The teacher's baby with the convulsions is much improved and has not convulsed for nearly twenty-four hours. The patient with the in-operable cancer of the stomach has died. I have scheduled

107

six patients for surgery tomorrow during the course of the morning.

10:45: Coffee break. Ann Saf comes in to talk about tomorrow's surgery cases. We agree on the scheduling, decide on anesthesia in each case, and try to set up the cases in such a way as to use our limited staff in the most efficient way. Just as Ann leaves, Greta Engborg comes in with a problem concerning the utilization of our "sample" drugs. Periodically we get boxes of drugs from the United States, mostly free samples which deluge the practicing physician, and they sometimes present as much of a problem in disposal as they are a help. Some of the "samples" are drugs which are useless in our work here, but the majority are readily used, and we are thankful to get them, especially if they have been well-sorted before they get here.

11:10: I am seeing the first outpatient when the noise begins. At first I assume that it is the relatives of the baby, but a glance out the window shows me that this is not the case.

For long periods of time I can forget that I am living in a culture radically different from my own. I eat, sleep, work, in much the same way that I do at home. My close associations are mainly with other Americans and educated Africans. But once in a while something pulls me up short and I realize that the people around me are different, in culture, in responses to natural happenings.

For instance, the wailing of the three women which can be heard outside the office window. One ancient crone, dressed only from the waist down in coal black, bends and weaves and cries in a loud piercing screech, on and on, endlessly. Another tall, stately woman dances a shuffling two-step, hands on top of her head, wailing "wa-*ah*, wa-*ah*, wa-*ah*," also endlessly, interrupted now and then with a "hoo, hoo, hoo, hoo," and again a singsong lament in Kinylamba. A third, more active, strides up and down the sand road, hands on her head, wailing and crying, now stopping to blow her nose against her finger, again ululating in a high staccato soprano like the American Indian on the warpath. Now she stops and the old crone takes off the outer black wrap-around garment and gives it to the younger well-dressed girl, who ties it around her waist with a black and orange polka-dot scarf.

The horrible wailing waxes and wanes. The blood runs chill, with the bright white of sun and the deep blue of sky forming a background for death. For these are mourners. A man has just died. I know this man. His disease has defied our attempts at diagnosis. Nothing fits. He gradually dies. This morning I said to Mr. Mangare, "This man is next," for an old Arab just died last night and the baby just died a few hours ago. My premonition now rings true.

The wailing fades away into the distance. The old crone lies prostrate in the sand. The younger women are down by the mission school, about a hundred yards away. The children continue their play; it is recess.

Now the contrast strikes home. Four teen-age student nurses, dressed in Sunday finery, come swinging down the pathway from the dormitory on their way to eleven o'clock services at the chapel. It is "Mkutano wakiroho"— Religious Emphasis Week—with three services a day. As they turn into the chapel, six more women come out of the hospital, single file, double-time, wailing, singing, weeping. They sway and turn and dance. One stops in her tracks, throws first one bare foot and then the other out behind her, chanting and wailing. This done about ten times, she rolls onto the ground kicking up a cloud of dust. The rest run on, picking up speed, until they meet the original three mourners coming from the school. The noise is now at a peak, the crescendo coming during the race down the road. One can sense a climax. All eyes are now on the sky. The women turn as if on a signal and with hands high in the air, trill and wail and chant. The noise is deafening. The group is now about fifty feet from my office. Polly tries to calm them. They ignore her. The tempo is picking up, the final event nears.

The doors of the hospital swing open and the body of the dead man, draped with the clothes he wore in life, is carried out on a wood and wicker bed. The women dance and cry and wail and trill and run toward the body and then around it. The men carry the bed down the road, with the women almost quiet now, running ahead. They disappear around the bend, where a path strikes off through the cornfields. I am left weak with drained emotion. I can see in my mind's eye the face of the dead man—sunken and yellow-white from his anemia and cachexia.

11:45: I have left the outpatients to wait while I witness this awesome spectacle. I have seen it many times before, but never with so many mourners, and never with so much noise. The impact on one's sensibilities is indescribable. It deadens one, it drains one, it crushes one's reason. It is no wonder that the Iramba Christians are embarrassed by this primitive display of atavistic emotions by their heathen friends and relatives.

11:50: I go through the outpatients quickly and promise Greta that I will see any of her problems from the OB clinic first thing in the afternoon.

12:40: Dinner.

1:30: Radio.

2:00-4:30: The afternoon goes quickly, with a steady flow of outpatients, a few problems from the morning's OB clinic, and an occasional minor surgery case.

4:30: I borrow a wheel from Alice Turnbladh's Volkswagen and drive out to get Dick Latchaw's car, still stranded out on the Sekenke road. Dick puts on the spare, and we drive back to Kiomboi, I with an eye on the rearview mirror to make sure Dick is still coming. No troubles.

5:45: Supper.

6:30-11:00: Uneventful evening. No calls. I finish with Barry Goldwater. A *Time* magazine has come today with his picture on the cover and I am able to compare the "conservative's conservative" of 1963 with his thoughts of 1960 as introduced in his book. Not much change, except he is hedging a little on his foreign aid beliefs, still not doing a flip-flop, but admitting that well-directed foreign aid for specific countries might be o.k. His ideas of doing away with the "graduated" income tax are appealing.

11:00: To bed, to sleep, perchance to dream.

3:30 A.M.: The dreams cut short, with Greta Engborg scratching on the screen at my window. She has been watching an OB for several hours with the head well down and the baby doing fine, but the girl has been in labor about twenty-four hours. I go down to the hospital and ask Greta to check her first to see if there has been any progress since she last examined her. There has been none. I check her and find her completely effaced and dilated, with the head showing. She has been "stuck" for about an hour and a half. Long enough. Too long. I put in a saddle block, scrub up, and put on outlet forceps, and with little trouble produce a rather quiet infant. A very few puffs, mouth-to-mouth, and everything is o.k.

4:15: Back to bed.

111

11

THE HOSPITAL—FRIDAY

7:00: As I sit in the radioroom awaiting the broadcast, Greta bursts in with the news that a patient brought from Barabaig by Louise Faust (four hard hours' drive, and Louise still jaundiced from hepatitis) has now refused surgery on the grounds that her husband has refused permission. Greta wants me to ask Lou on radio what we should do. I do, when my turn comes, and all Louise can say is that she is utterly disgusted, but that we had better not operate until she has a chance to talk to the husband. Cancel, I tell Greta, who makes a face.

7:15: Bacon and eggs. Edna has been able to buy three eggs and we distribute them evenly by scrambling them.

7:30: Vespers in the minor OR.

7:40: The first case is the twelve-year-old boy with a hernia and an undescended testicle. I sit and talk with him gently, glad that he is a schoolboy and knows Swahili, for if he knew only his tribal dialect I would have to talk through an interpreter, and rapport would be difficult if not impossible. I tell him we can put him to sleep, or I can stick a needle in his back and numb his lower body. He vehemently demands the needle, so we do a spinal anesthetic, something nearly unheard of in a child of this age in the United States. The surgery is uneventful.

8:45: The next case is a lady with KKKK disease and it is necessary to perform a total hysterectomy, as it is usually in this condition when it is far enough advanced to require surgery. I stay well outside the scarred down mass (mess?) of pelvic organs by entering the retroperitoneal space via the round ligaments, dissecting out both ureters, and remove the pelvic organs *in toto*.

10:15: Coffee break early today. There is a letter on the desk from Duke University to an African student, with application forms for entrance. Having lived there for two years, I ponder grimly the reaction a young African would have to life in Durham, North Carolina. I walk back over to the OR, and finding them not quite ready for the next case, stand at the main entrance watching the passing parade. Four women go past, with the inevitable loads of food on their heads, and cross the ramp to the cooking area. Students pass in and out on errands, the girls murmuring demurely, "Good morning, doctor," the boys more open and smiling. Ambulatory inpatients stroll around; others sit idly with friends and relatives on the hard dry yellow grass; others, outpatients mostly, sit outside the drugroom waiting for medicine.

Nosoro Sefu, a friend of mine from the government offices at the Boma, drives up with a man who had been caught stealing and who tried to escape by jumping out of the back of the moving truck; he has a broken nose and possibly a broken arm. Nosoro tells me he is going elephant hunting tomorrow over in Wakindiga country. I tell him to bring me a couple of fifty pound tusks. He laughs, "Sure, doctor!" That much ivory would be worth more than he makes in several months.

I hear a sudden swirl of fifes and flutes and the roll of drums, and look over toward the African primary school where a hundred children in pink and tan are marching around the soccer field. Oh, how they love to march! Soon they break up in order to play games for a while before going back to their classrooms. I fall into conversation

with an Mtaturu young man from the Wembere Plains
with ivory bracelets from wrists to elbows and a fantastically complicated necklace of copper wires and 5¢ copper
coins. He tells me he is a herder of cattle and owns more
than a hundred. At an average of a hundred shillings a
cow, his walking bank account of ten thousand shillings
amounts to about $1,430. His leather sandals and simple
black robe thrown loosely about his lean muscular body
belie his actual wealth. His head is shaved in front like
a Barabaig's, and the tattooed markings circling his eyes
give him the appearance of wearing large clear-glass
spectacles. His eyes are exceedingly intelligent, and I am
much impressed by his deliberate mien, without false
pride, but with an obvious sense of his own abilities and
worth. The thought fleets through my mind that I would
probably like this man as a friend. He is about my age.
When he walks, he is straight as an arrow, his robe billowing in the dry-season wind.

10:40: A glomectomy is scheduled next. As I have stood
talking, I saw the patient moved along the ramp from
Ward C into the OR. Now Mr. Mangare, who has been
making rounds, tells me that the baby we bronchoscoped
two nights ago is having trouble again. We were about to
send him home, since he had had no trouble. I go to see
him, and he is having a violent coughing spell as I enter
the ward. He is obviously blue around the lips, and even
his ebony skin looks darker. I send a student to the OR
to tell Ann Saf to cancel the glomectomy and get the
endoscopic equipment ready. Meanwhile I listen to the
lungs of the baby. Both are aerating well, but a coarse
rattling sound is audible through all the lung fields. I
am perplexed. The findings are that of a foreign body
lying in the main windpipe, but could I have missed seeing something that big the other night?

11:10: Mr. Mangare and two students hold the baby

114

and I slip in the three and a half millimeter bronchoscope. I am somewhat startled to see a nearly intact half-peanut lying just inside the vocal chords in the trachea. I can reach it rather easily through the scope with long forceps and pull it out with the scope, forceps, and peanut all in one unit. The baby immediately lets out a yell, the character now changed, without the rattling sound. His lips and ears pink up. One of the students picks him up and takes him out to his mother who is waiting anxiously in the minor surgery room by the admitting desk. I sit wonderingly, but happy, trying to figure out how that peanut eluded me the other night. The only way I could have missed seeing it would be that it lay high in the trachea that night also, and my scope passed over it.

11:20: Since this has taken such a short time, we go ahead with the originally scheduled glomectomy.

12 noon: A skin graft has been set up in the minor room, and Mr. Paulo and I go in there to do it. We change gowns and gloves, without contaminating ourselves. I adjust the long flat blade in the brackets of the small graft machine, set the reading at 12 on each side, assuring us of a split-thickness graft 12 microns in thickness, and rub down the donor site on the leg with sterile vaseline. The patient has been given a general anesthetic. I place the machine on the leg, Mr. Paulo stretches the skin behind it, and by coordinating a downward and forward pressure with my left hand and a rapid back-and-forth movement with my right hand, a translucent, almost white, filmy sheet of skin curls over the moving blade and is picked up gently with tissue forceps by Mr. Msambe. We take several full lengths of skin in this manner and lay them on a slightly moist saline sponge for protection while the donor site is wrapped and the burned area is draped into the field. The burn is red with the scarlet of millions of transparent capillaries forming a base for the

115

new skin. The graft is tenderly lifted from the sponge, placed shiny-side down on the burn, and gently teased flat with forceps. Within minutes the new skin has "glued" itself to its new base, indicating that the donor site was ready. The graft is nicked with the scalpel in several places to allow fluid to exude (pie bakers would recognize this maneuver!) and the wound dressed.

12:40: Home for lunch.

1:30: Radio.

1:45: We have three more cases scheduled. The first is the epileptic Barabaig with the multiple burn contractures. Under spinal anesthesia I am able to straighten the leg within thirty-five degrees of normal by means of a Z-shaped incision, a small local pedicle flap, and a free skin graft from the other leg. Presumably, with the scar tissue gone, we will now be able to straighten the leg gradually in a cast over a period of four to six weeks.

3:15: The second case is a suprapubic prostatectomy, and all goes well. We are unable to do the more modern (transurethral) operation, so we fall back on the time-honored and still satisfactory procedure of total removal of the gland in cases of urinary obstruction.

4:30: Mr. Mangare asks me to see the postoperative patient from three days ago who had so much pain in her incision. He is worried. I examine her abdomen and am also worried. In fact I am greatly concerned, for beneath the skin surrounding the surgical wound I can feel the ominous crackle of free gas. Gas gangrene. My mind flashes uncontrollably to the last patient I had with gas gangrene, and from whom, in curious coincidence, I have received a letter only two days ago. This other patient, from Elk Mound near Eau Claire, lost his leg and very nearly his life, but in his case we could obliterate the source of infection by amputating the leg. In this patient we can hardly remove her entire abdominal wall.

5:15: Under general anesthesia, I remove the three-day old stitches and great bubbles of nauseous-smelling gas escape. The muscles of the abdomen are greenish-black with the color of death, and the only thing that can be done is to make multiple incisions through all the dead tissue and insert drains and catheters through which hydrogen-peroxide can be instilled to bring death-dealing oxygen to this organism which can only live in an oxygen-free environment. No sutures are placed. I write orders for massive doses of polyvalent gas bacilli antitoxin, and penicillin. (All to no avail, for the patient died seven hours after surgery.)

6:30: Outside the putrefaction of the operating room, the sun still shines brightly, as it did two hours before, and the odor of the early blossoming jacarandas is carried strongly on the wind. Through this golden light, death has walked in and made himself at home.

7:00: The blood-red sun throws the acacias and palm trees into stark relief as I walk slowly up the path to home. Death is practically never a pretty thing, but this way of going is particularly unattractive. I suppose a doctor, more than anybody, hates disease and death; if he didn't, he wouldn't fight so hard against it. But he must develop a superficial callousness to it, must seem to be immune to it, must not become emotionally involved with it; for those who do, suffer too much. And when a desperately ill patient does pull through, against all odds, one must assume an attitude of, "Well, you didn't think we'd let him die, did you?"

7:10: Supper. Edna and the children have already eaten, so Dick and I eat alone.

7:30: Radio.

8-11:00: I run through some of the pictures I have taken for Dick and we spend the rest of the evening talking about his paper.

117

12

THE SINGING SPEARS IN THE VALLEY OF THE BARABAIG

We had the eerie feeling that we were hanging some-where between a dust-filled limbo and a sun-baked hell. Heaven and earth were only figments of the imagination of some unknown idiot. This was all that there was that was real.

As far as the eye could see was a flat, cracked gray expanse of nothingness and the humming singing engine of the Land Rover contributed to the hypnosis. Occasionally along the periphery of our private world a shimmering lake with ghostly bushes and short stubby trees could be discerned, but always as we drove closer to the water, it receded as fast as we approached, until the thirsty lake-bed soaked up the last remaining drop and we drove through the water spewing dust from our wheels.

We were driving through a dry lake bed in the eastern branch of the great Rift Valley, that huge cleft in the geography of East Africa that extends from the south through Tanganyika, Kenya, the Sudan, and ends in the Red Sea, some saying that the Red Sea itself is merely a continuation of this gigantic rift. We had climbed in first gear upwards from Singida, center of the district famed throughout the Africa-conscious world for its legendary lion-men, along the top of the ridge to the turn-off. To the right lay the ten-mile road to the Catholic Mission Hospital called Makiungu; straight ahead was our road to Mgori and thence to Barabaig; and to the left continued the main road to Katesh, Babati, Arusha, Moshi, Nairobi. The roads behind us and to left and right stayed on the ridge. The road ahead dropped us in a series of steep descents into the Rift Valley.

We stopped to see Orv and June Nyblade at the mission station at Mgori about three fourths of the way down to the valley floor, then pushed on through the village of Mgori into the valley itself. The track was dry, contrasting interestingly with the sea of mud we had driven through six months before in this same place. The eight-mile stretch from Mgori to Ngimu was perhaps a mile off to the side of the very bottom of the valley, so that we could see across the nearly treeless expanse. The Turu bomas were scattered around the valley and on its sides, green rings distributed haphazardly on the brown earth. ("Boma" is the Swahili word referring to any raised structure which is used for protection, such as an enclosure of trees or stakes.) Along the road we passed women with huge baskets of sweet potatoes; men in long kanzus walking slowly along discussing, no doubt, the coming rains and the prospects of the harvest; and cows and goats on the roadside grass.

Passing through Ngimu, a village of perhaps two dozen shops and houses, we spotted the storage place which we had seen filled with bags of grain donated by the people of the United States to the people of Africa during last year's famine. Past Ngimu, we were soon crowded in on both sides of the narrow track by dense bush, known to contain one of the heaviest concentrations of lions in all East Africa. We saw none that day. Then out of the bush again into the open plain, glad for the freedom of vision

119

after the claustrophobic bush. The greenringed Turu bomas disappeared as if by magic and in their place emerged the dry brown bomas of the Barabaig. And soon we could see the huge herds of cattle and goats, with the young Barabaig boys tending them standing on one leg, the other foot resting on the kneecap of the supporting leg. Each wore a russet-colored robe loosely thrown over his shoulder as the only garment and carried a small brown circular buffalo-hide or eland-hide shield in one hand and a six-foot, razor-sharp spear in the other.

In the distance we could see clouds whirling, blown by the merciless wind through the sun-dried air. In that other world across the seas, this would be mist blown from the whitecaps of a blue-white lake, riding high like clouds on a mountain. In this parched world of the valley of the Barabaig, those mists were clouds of gray-white dust from the bottom of a lake. As we came closer, we dropped off the sides of the ridge into the dust, on a two-wheeled track, and out onto the lake bed itself. Soon we were streaking along at fifty miles an hour, no longer tied by our wheels to the bumpy, rutted, teeth-jarring track, flying instead like the dust around us. It was here we imagined ourselves in our own private world of flatness, dryness, nothingness, with miraged lakes all around us, peopled with writhing, twisting gargoyle forms that vanished when approached too closely. The illusions of forms and animals and people and water were so real that twice we turned off from our line of flight to investigate these supposed realities, only to find them evanesce into dust and vapor, leaving us stunned and incredulous.

Fortunately, the lake was not long, the traverse taking perhaps twenty minutes, and eventually we saw the solid shining aluminum roofs of the mission station on the hills ahead. The lake shore passed, the track wound through green-yellow plains dotted with herds of cattle and goats and clumps of acacia thorns, and up a hundred feet or more to the mission station, which consists of church, dispensary, school, and pastor's house. The missionaries here are Hal Faust and his wife, Louise. As we pulled into the yard, we were greeted by the usual crowd of Barabaigs, children and adults. We pushed the doors of the car open against the press of brown and brown-clad bodies and went into the house. The tall lean men with their 12 o'clock haircuts (front half shaved off) stuck their heads in all the open windows of the Land Rover, taking it all in and talking rapidly in their own dialect about the wonders within. One of the wonders was a medium-sized eland skin, dried and stiff, almost filling the back of the car. I had shot it some six months before and had now brought it along to have one of the Barabaigs make a shield for me.

The Barabaigs are a tribe of approximately fifteen thousand people, a relatively small tribe. They are related closely to the Masai in looks, custom, dress. Some thousands of years ago, a group of people from the upper Nile Valley in Egypt migrated downwards into the Sudan, then Kenya and Tanganyika. This group divided gradually into two major tribes, the Masai and the Nandi. The Masai now occupy a huge open bush area in southern Kenya and northern Tanganyika and have been extensively studied and photographed. The other major division, the Nandi, has subdivided again a number of times and one of the major divisions is the Barabaig, or Datog, as they call themselves.

They are a primitive tribe in comparison to other tribes in central Tanganyika. For the most part they are cattle herders, and, like the Masai, are content with no schooling and are resistant to all attempts to "improve" them. They tend to feel superior to the white man and to the other Africans.

We were welcomed warmly by Louise and, a few moments later, by Hal. Hal, recovering from a long serious illness, was well hidden behind a luxuriant full beard, sunglasses, and a wide-brimmed brown hat with one side turned up, and we couldn't tell if he looked more like General Grant, Ernest Hemmingway, or a retired Kentucky colonel.

After a delicious dinner of impala steaks, Louise and I went down to the dispensary. I had been there several times before, and I greeted the tribal dresser, Mr. Joeli Mbutu, the translator Marko, the nurse's aid Beatrice, and others of the staff. The physical plant itself consists of two main buildings, one with three rooms for screening outpatients, and one with four rooms with four to five beds each for holding inpatients. Both buildings are constructed of kilned brick and concrete floors. Waiting patients crowded around the buildings, the men around the examination building, expecting to be seen first; the women sitting on the cement ramp connecting the rooms of the holding unit. At first glance, all the men look alike, with long lean distinctly semitic or nilotic brown faces with the 12 o'clock haircut, earlobes plugged with ivory pieces about the size of a quarter, necklaces of various kinds (coins, shells, beads, even occasionally teeth or small bones), russet-brown robes over their bodies, long staves (spears are left lined up against the back of the building), long legs, feet shod in rubber (from old auto tires) or leather sandals. But as one studies them more closely, one sees the individuals emerge from the mass, and all the various types of personalities known to us become apparent. There is the sensitive, shy, retiring man with an apology on his lips for being sick; the arrogant hunter with ivory from his elephant and claws from his lion; the village clown, unable to say anything without making everyone laugh; the tubercular, the old, the hypochondriac, the minimizer. A whole yardful of individuals with the aspirations, hopes, ambitions, trials, sicknesses, and mother-in-law troubles of all of mankind.

One gets the same impression of uniformity with the first glance at the women. Short hair, shaved off the front half of the scalp; blue-tattooed dotted-line circles around the eyes; long lean faces; earrings or plugs of many varieties; shiny copper rings concentrically encircling the neck like the grid of an electric stove; brown leather stole-like skin over the shoulders laced or pinned at the neck, leaving the breasts bare; arms heavy with brass or iron bracelets from elbow to hand; a long skirt of the same brown leather as the cape, fitting the hips tightly and swaying seductively in dance or walk; and sandals of leather. Most of the women had on their prettiest skins made soft and brown from many hours of softening by curing in cows' urine, then worked with the teeth until pliable as chamois, then fantastically and intricately beaded with tiny multicolored beads.

But, as with the men, the appearance of sameness is only illusory. Look closer. You will find the middle-aged matron, wise as only matriarchs can be; the flirtatious, laughing belle; the sly weaver of webs, and the gossip. Here also are the truly sick, with wan faces, wasted limbs, or fevered eyes; the tired; the discouraged; the curious; the suspicious. All womankind is represented here, if only you will look closer.

We decided to examine the women first, while the MA screened the men to see if he could resolve some of the problems without me. We went into the small dim examining room in the inpatient building. Louise worked outside, trying to match up patients with their history cards. I worked inside with Beatrice, who is herself one of the few baptized Barabaigs. She is one of the few Barabaig women who knows Swahili, and therefore she was able to translate from the Barabaig dialect into Swahili for me. Almost all the women had pelvic complaints, some serious and requiring surgery for their correction. We made arrangements to take one of them back to Kiomboi with us the next day and encouraged the others to make plans to go there as soon as possible.

When we had finished with the women, we went over to the outpatient building and saw the men. Here Marko, also a baptized Christian Barabaig, translated for me, although some of the Barabaig men have learned Swahili in their contacts with the world outside their valley. Marko is invaluable to the work of the mission. He is young, probably about twenty, with a quick smile, eager aggressive attitude, and he has learned to keep records and figure a little. I have seen pictures of him taken only a few years ago, with ivory plugs in his ears, brown robe over his shoulder, spear and shield in his hands. The ivory is gone now, leaving huge holes in the lobes (somehow I can't help but mourn their passing), and he has adopted the more convenient shirt and pants for work around the dispensary. I have seen him handle a spear, the hollow ground head and the tapering wooden tip quivering into life as he vibrated it to balance it by grasping it with fingers and hand held like a violinist's on his strings. If one were to write a story of Marko and the Barabaigs, it should be called "The Singing Spear." This is what the spear seems to do, first lying dormant as wood and steel; then awakening to the sensitive fingers playing a song on its six-foot length.

Marko had just taken a wife when we visited the valley this time. We met her, a beautiful little girl with poignancy in her eyes, dressed not in her native beaded skins, but more like the Isanzu or Iramba women, in brightly colored shuka and plastic sandals. They made a handsome pair, he so tall and strong and masculine, she so young and lithe and feminine. Despite their change in dress, I can more easily envision him with the singing spear and ivory ear plugs and her in the leaping swaying dance of the Barabaigs, than I can in westernized clothing and more civilized surroundings.

Marko is not an evangelist; he is not even an educated layman. But from my observations, he is an integral part of the Barabaig mission. As I see it, Hal and Louise Faust utilize at least four specific ways to reach the Barabaig people with the gospel. One major way is by means of a ten-minute service at the dispensary each morning, usually held by Louise. She speaks to the waiting patients in Swahili, which is understood by some of the men, and her message is then translated into the Barabaig dialect by Beatrice or Marko. A second avenue of contact with these people is in the school, which was started in 1962 after much deliberation and many problems. The potential here is tremendous and does not need elaboration. The third route is of course the personal contact of the missionary and his wife with the individual people—both in the spoken word and in the unspoken witness. And the fourth way is the contact of Barabaig Christians with their own people. And it is in this realm that Marko is so important. Despite his break from many of the customs of his people, he is still accepted and respected by his family and people.

The sun was not far from the horizon when we finished with the last patient, but Hal had heard that there was some kind of a ceremony going on in one of the bomas only three miles from the mission. We grabbed the cameras, piled in their Land Rover with Marko and his wife coming along for the ride, circled the nearly dry swamp below the hill and found the boma we were looking for. The bomas of the Turu are made from large stakes (which invariably grow branches) arranged in a circle or ellipse, giving the boma a green living appearance. The bomas of the Irambas are made of smaller, taller sticks which are arranged in a more square or rectangular shape. The bomas of the Barabaigs are made circular, low, and are invariably brownish gray because they are made of piles of brush and thorn-bush which dry up and never take root. Inside the circular "fence" are the houses, with the framework of each made of sturdy forked branches with ridgepoles laid in the forks. The roof of each house, rarely over five feet high and often lower, is made of intertwined branches and packed with mud on the outside. The walls are made of thin sticks and then plastered on the inside with cow dung—a variation of the mud and wattle walls of other tribes. There are usually no windows and the only light comes from a small door at one corner. For these outdoor people, a house is a place in which to sleep, to take shelter from the rain, and to store grain.

The boma we came to was no different from others I had seen, but we soon found that it held a special significance for the people, since this was the boma of the medicine man. He was not in sight when we arrived, and all the other men had also disappeared. About a dozen women were standing in a circle just outside the main house chanting an interminable fragment of song over and over again, their bodies swaying forward from the hips in time with the music. Periodically, the younger girls with the heavy iron bracelets would rub arm against arm, also in time to the music, making a not unpleasant ringing sound. The sun was now on the horizon, throwing a golden pastel glow over the scene, already an almost pure study in golds and browns.

I noticed after some moments that the women were not chanting idly over nothing. On the ground in front of them, almost hidden by their tightly pressed legs and bodies, was a hide of an animal, probably a cow, which approaches sacredness in the Barabaig culture. On the hide were a group of water gourds. Then I noticed a loose pile of sandals lying there also, and shortly thereafter one of the women tied the sandals tightly together with a leather thong.

The youngest of the girls, possibly fifteen years old, whom we later identified as the medicine man's wife, took a half gourd filled with a white oil and went from one woman to another, smearing foreheads of all with the oil, and also the breasts of those with children on their backs. We also learned later that this oil had been especially blessed by the medicine man and therefore was in itself a powerful medicine and had magical powers. Louise Faust told me that she could not watch this oil-smearing ceremony without remembering the many references in the Bible to the religious ceremony of "anointing the head with oil."

I was filming this part of the ceremony when I noticed Hal off to one side talking to a young lad named Sampson who had been baptized not long before. In the few seconds I had looked away a sudden change had taken place in the ring of women. Apparently from nowhere the medicine man had materialized and was now on hands and knees inside the circle. He was dressed all in black, and in the now waning light I could hardly see him, but I could hear him. He was taking huge mouthfuls of milk from a gourd and spewing it out in great profusion over the gourds and sandals on the skin. In about thirty seconds he was done and disappeared.

Now, taking an ebony stave with a forked end, the wife strode out of the boma. The other women followed silently, and all disappeared around the far side. This was apparently the climax of the ceremony, for in a few moments the young wife returned, followed by one of the other women. The rest went off to their own bomas.

We were curious to know just what they had been doing, and Marko informed us that it was a prayer ritual to the gods. It was a general "asking" type of ceremony—for rain, for good hunts, for fertility for the women, for protection of their children. We would call it a prayer meeting, and one wonders a little if these people might have been praying to the same God that we do, with a somewhat altered liturgy, but certainly asking for the same things.

During the drive home through the lingering dusk, we saw a majestic impala and his doe striding haughtily out of the bush across a small grassy swale. He had a slight limp, but this only seemed to make him the more proud, as if he had been wounded in honest combat. My memory flashed to the two impala I had come upon one day fighting it out to the death. With their horns alternatingly crashing together and locking head to head, their white flags flicking desperately to add a slightly comic note to the mortal conflict, they stood now glaring at each other, then ramming head on, then down on fore-knees, dust swirling in the air, around and around looking for an opening.

We drove across the swale, crossing behind the proud pair, and then stopped the car to let Hal's dog get a little run. We stood in the half-light, listening to the beginnings of the night-sounds in the bush. Hal stabbed us with the remark that we would not ever forget this peacefulness even after our return to the raucousness of city life, and that this above all else would keep calling us back to Africa.

13

THE SPIRIT OF THE DONKEY

The old woman watched the dancers with unconcealed merriment, dreaming back through uncountable years to her own youth. How long had it been? Dry season had followed wet, and wet the dry, until it was no longer possible to reckon time at all. She watched her eldest son, standing tall and straight, with handsome sensuous face, bronze-colored skin shining in the red sun's dying rays, slim strong muscles aching to take his turn. His sandals lay on the ground at the old woman's feet, scattered carelessly with a dozen other pairs. His rust-colored robe hung loosely over his shoulders reaching to mid-thigh, swinging gracefully with each movement, and revealing the lack of any other hindering clothes. He held in his right hand the six-foot staff of his rank. The front half of his head was shaved, the back half cropped short, and in his pierced ears were the ivory plugs from his first elephant kill.

Suddenly, he strode quickly to the center of the ring of people, and without a word or change in facial expression, leaped high in the air, body held rigid, bouncing a dozen times straight upwards, unbelievably high, then as suddenly turning and returning to his place with the other young men, scarcely seeming to notice the swaying bouncing dance of the young girl who had come out to meet him. The rhythm of the dance was incredibly steady, the beat being carried by the simultaneous crash of stave on shield and stave on ground wielded by a man with a headress of brown-dyed baboon hair, and with the cadence counted with a persistent high-pitched "Eee-yi, Eee-yi, Eee-yi-yi." The weird effect of crashing shield and foreshortened yelp continued on and on, each warrior taking his turn.

Suddenly the tempo changed. The girls, in their beautifully beaded dresses of animal skins, ceased their participation, as one by one the young men ran to the center of the circle and with great seriousness threw down on the ground a number of carved sticks. This was the dance of the hunt, and the number of sticks thrown down indicated the most dangerous animal the hunter had killed —eight for rhino, nine for elephant, ten for lion, and eleven—for man.

Hangali Mwarada, the old woman's son, stood watching the younger and the less adventuresome of the warriors, advancing one at a time, throwing down their four or five sticks; finally came the braver and stronger with their seven or eight sticks. Then three men with nine sticks. Then it was Hangali's turn and he leaped into the ring of brown-clad Barabaigs, threw down one stick, then another, on up to ten, for he had killed a lion with his spear.

His mother drew a deep proud breath and spat luxuriously on the ground. This was a son of whom to be proud. She remembered he had always been strong. As a newborn babe he had survived the force-feeding of corn gruel with scarcely a cry, while others whimpered constantly as the harsh foods cramped the unaccustomed bellies, and many others wasted away and died. And as a lad, he was always in the lead in games of skill and strength. Oh, he was a son to be proud of. He was almost certain to become venerated and be one of those accorded a burial in a tower of clay with the skin of a black bull around him, the body of the bull having been thrown to the hyenas and vultures as compensation for not having the man's body, as was the custom. She would not be alive, but she could picture it now—first the hole in the ground, then Hangali's body placed in the hole after sitting three days in his widow's hut, then the black skin thrown over his shoulders, and finally the clay packed around him to begin the formation of the tower. Then, as the months passed, would come the monthly gathering of the entire clan in the specially constructed camp, with pleas to the gods, dancing, and drinking of honey beer, and the gradual enlargement of the clay tomb until it reached upwards ten feet or more. And after nine months, the day would come on which his spirit would leave the body, having been nourished during the entire time by milk and honey beer poured into the hole in the side of the tower. On that final day the four greatest warriors would bring in the mat of specially grown grass which had been lovingly grown and protected from animal contaminations and finally woven into the green mat to be placed on the top of the tower as the old man's hair. Then the eldest son, not even born yet as the old woman dreamed, would climb to the top and offer his prayers to the gods for the safe journey of his father's spirit to the Spirit-world.

The old woman's dreams went on and on. This was her son, unblemished. And she, as this man's mother, could always bask in the glow of his strength. Always.

The light was fading rapidly. The older people, not as concerned with the dance, began to blow on the embers of the fires, and soon the little circular village glowed red with the light of the large cooking fires. The dancing stopped, the crashing staves and shields were stilled, and the men and girls retired to their separate houses to join their families for supper.

Was there ever such peace? The crackling of dried acacias burning, the low soughing wind in the thornbush, the plaintive cry of a lone hyena, a murmur of voices, an occasional burst of laughter, the cry of a child.

Suddenly, there was a scream, then muted silence. A sobbing sound, achingly painful. It was the old woman, mother of Hangali. She had tripped and fallen, her left leg thudding into the roaring flames of the fire. Hangali rushed to her, brushed off the bits of glowing embers that had adhered to her charred flesh. The whole episode lasted only a moment. The pain began to subside, and the old woman cautiously raised up to look at her leg. The outside of her lower leg and foot was very painful, and she could see the changes in the skin through the white ashes from the fire that covered the leg with a fine powder. She was ashamed at having cried out, especially now that she saw the minor extent of the injury.

Hangali spoke gently to her, "This will be very painful tonight, mother. We will not be able to gather the proper leaves because of the darkness. I will send the sisters early in the morning."

"Thank you, son of Mwarada. I will endure the night knowing that my great hunter thinks of me."

The night was long, and the leg throbbed continuously as it began to swell. By morning it was greatly thickened and weeping great drops of yellow fluid except over the foot and outside of the calf where it stayed curiously dry and hard. The younger children were of the opinion that the dry part was not burned badly, but the old woman knew better. The dry hard skin was like many others she had seen, and she knew that that part would be the last to heal, perhaps many months from now.

The healing leaves were found, dried ones which could be crumbled into a powder and spread on the burned areas, and then held there with a soothing poultice of moist red clay.

For the first few days all went well. The clay dried and began to break off, taking the upper layers of dead skin with it, leaving a tender red wet wound underneath. This was again treated with dried leaves and mud and soon showed signs of healing, except for the hard skin on the foot and side of the calf. After about a week, this began to turn black, and the edges began to separate from the rest of the skin as the normal healing processes tried to slough away the dead skin.

For three weeks, the old woman limped about, doing her work as best she could, but mostly just sitting with her back to the wattled side of the house. A strange lassitude began to creep up on her, and soon she started having fever and a severe throbbing headache. She began to notice twitching of her muscles, especially about the face. Her mind began to wander, and she could be heard mumbling incoherently. Within twenty-four hours, she was nearly unconscious and began to convulse in great shaking spasms, head thrown back, back arched, mouth held in a tight teeth-baring grimace. It was obvious to Hangali that she had been visited by the evil spirits of the donkey, and he called in the most powerful doctor to exorcise them.

Day followed night, and night the day, and the old woman lay in the corner of the house in her peculiar contorted position, periodically convulsing until her breath nearly stopped and she became as dead. Then the visitation of the spirits would leave, in response to the chanting of the doctor, and she would subside into deeper coma, still held in her arching vise. Hangali forced water and gruel and honey down the sides of her mouth through the gaps in her teeth, since he could not open her mouth even with his great strength. His mind flashed to the hated Turus to the west who knocked out the two front teeth of all their children so as to be able to feed them when these dreaded spirits came.

Meanwhile, the burned leg lay in the dirt, forgotten, and during the seizures it ground against the dirt until the dead skin was all rubbed off and the dirt rubbed into the wound. It began to swell and redden and drain, and the odor from it pervaded the little house. Little by little, the old woman straightened, her eyes opened, her neck began to bend forward, and her mouth relaxed. And after about two weeks, Hangali gave the doctor a cow in payment and sent him away. The old woman would live.

Hangali and his sisters dragged the old woman out of the darkness into the light and propped her up against the house. Only then did they see the burned leg, and with horror they looked from it to the face of the old woman, now seeing for the first time the future for their mother, the future which had been hidden in the darkness of the house. For now most of the leg below the knee was black with the color of death.

Hangali motioned to the others, and they withdrew beyond the circle of houses. Hangali said, "I am the eldest son. It is therefore my duty to tell our mother what has happened and what must therefore be done. Do you all agree that it must be done?"

All nodded their assent. "It must be done."

"Leave me then."

Hangali sat down in the shade of an acacia tree to think. His mind slowly drifted back through the years, picking out incidents here and there that tied him to his mother. How could he tell his own mother that she could no longer associate with him, nor anyone else in Barabaig-land? But he had no alternative. This was their custom—more than that—it was their obligation—to sequester from them anyone with deformities to protect themselves from the evil which must emanate from a deformed body.

Slowly, he got to his feet, words forming in his mind. I will tell her right out, he thought, no wasted words or emotions. Then we will carry her out into the forest and leave her. It will be better that way. And in the morning, or the next morning, or the next, she will be gone. We must carry her far enough that we cannot hear her scream when the hyenas come.

His eyes downcast, his whole demeanor so uncharacteristic of his usual proud self, Hangali approached his mother, and squatted in the dust at his mother's feet.

Before he could speak, she opened her eyes, and her mind now clear, she said, "You have come."

"I have come."

"I know why you have come," quietly.

"You know," with a great heaving sigh.

"I know."

"We cannot do otherwise, Mother."

"That I also know, Hangali, son of Mwarada."

They sat thus as the sun passed overhead and began to descend. Then the old woman said, "Build me a hut."

"I will do so."

"Build me a fire."

"That I can also do, the first night."

"Yes, the first night." She looked at him with eyes clouded with mournful longing.

"I will live, Hangali."

This old woman has courage, Hangali thought to himself. But she cannot live. The hyenas will smell that rotting leg, and as soon as the fire goes out they will finish her. And she will not be able to gather wood to keep the fire going. And none of us from the village can approach close enough to her to give her wood. Or food. Even if at first she can find wood close by, she will soon become weak with hunger, and will not be able to continue.

The old woman read his thoughts through his eyes. "You can approach me close enough to leave food and wood, and I will drag myself to it after you have left it. You will see. I will live, Hangali, son of Mwarada!"

"Prepare yourself, Mother. We will go tomorrow morning when it is light enough to follow the trail."

The old woman dragged herself into the hut. She was now unclean, and all those who now came into contact with her would necessarily undergo strict purifying ceremonies which would continue for weeks, and for Hangali who had actually touched her, months. Her heart was heavy, but as much for her family as for herself because of what they must endure, and it was not their fault. She considered for a moment what she would need in the wilderness, alone. A gourd for water, a half gourd for collecting food, a machete for cutting wood, a dried impala skin for her bed, a few other things. . . .

The next morning, they carried the old woman on a skin between two poles into the deepest part of the wilderness, where no one lived and no one ever went except to hunt.

Hangali did not need to build a hut for his mother, having found a cave-like opening in the rocks on the side of a hill. He placed his mother on the skin inside and built a fire of dried twigs near the entrance.

The old woman watched the preparation of her death house.

We shall not try to fathom the emotions which came to her at this time, just as we will not probe the mind of her son, his actions following the blind patterning of his instincts developed through countless centuries of the survival of the fittest. He had no facilities with which to reason out this situation, though his mind be as keen as an Einstein. His was the unthinking obedience to the laws of the tribe, these laws evolving through trial and error, constantly influenced by the witch doctors and the medicine men, who in turn were influenced by what they saw, or, more to the point, what they thought they saw in the world about them. The reader may visualize as well as the writer what long-forgotten events might have promulgated this particular custom among the Barabaig people. One may rightly wonder why the loss of any part of the body, even the tip of a finger, should cause various degrees of ostracism from the family group and thence the tribe, up to and including total ostracism. Is the deformed one less able to function in helping to preserve the collective life of the tribe? Or is it the deformation of the individual's physical beauty itself that is repugnant to the group?

Into the cave they carried the old woman. And left her.

If the relating of this story were a figment of the imagination, it might well end here, without climax or anticlimax, with the gruesome death of the old woman. But, truth being stranger than fiction, it does not end here. Indeed, it does not. For the events related here happened eighteen years ago, and just a few months ago, I saw the old woman. She tells a straight-forward story of how she survived, as she promised she would.

She lived in perpetual fear, especially at night. She recalls the first few months as one would relive a nightmare in the light of morning. She dragged herself around the bush each day, collecting the twigs and branches she would need each night to ward off the hyenas. On her forays she would eat berries, when they were in season. She ate the bittersweet fruits of the baobabs. She ate roots, and in the rainy season she boiled up the long grass and ate it, as one would eat spinach. From time to time her son would risk ostracism himself by coming to within a few hundred yards of her cave and leaving small sacks of millet and corn for her use.

Graudally her leg dried, black and dead, and the marvelous powers of healing inherent in all of us sloughed the greater part of the foot and lower leg off, and skin covered the end of the raw bone. But she still could not walk and apparently did not think to make a crutch in order to hobble on her one good leg. Sometime in the first weeks a hyena actually did enter her cave and take off part of her other foot, which also healed in time. So for fourteen of these eighteen years she never left the ground.

As the years passed, she became a creature of the forest more so even than she was before, existing on the natural foods she found about her, animal-like, and alone.

This was the way Louise Faust found her. Stories of this denizen of the bush came to the Fausts during their first years in the new mission in the valley of the Barabaig, and they hardly credited them with truthfulness. Gradually, they came to believe them and sought her out. And they found her. She would not leave her "home," so Louise began to visit her periodically, taking little presents of food and clothing, and eventually, crutches. The old woman at first was suspicious of the white woman and her intentions, but gradually she came to trust, then love her, as do all the Barabaigs who have come to know her. She tried the crutches, failed in her early attempts to use them, and tossed them aside. Louise forced her to use them and eventually persuaded her to leave her forest home.

The old woman now lives in a small room built onto

the dispensary. She has become a Christian, and has been reconciled to her son.

Her son? What has become of Hangali, son of Mwarada? For a long time he was afraid to break with the powerful traditions of his tribe, but gradually he too came to trust Hal and Louise Faust. At the present time (October, 1963) he is studying Christianity and is building a house not far from the mission where he and his mother will live.

There are those who would say, "Leave the African to work out his own salvation. Do not introduce Christianity or education to him. It will only make him unhappy and neurotic," and on and on.

Is the old woman less happy now, since Christian love and compassion have entered her life? Was she happier in her loneliness, in her never-ending fear, in her separation from human companionship?

And her son. Was he happier in his dung-plastered hut, remembering the mother he had carried to her death? Was he happier before he was educated to the fact that nothing terrible befalls those who minister to a deformed person?

Were these two lives better off before Hal and Louise Faust came to Barabaig-land?

14

EASTER SUNDAY

The sound of clear, high, girlish voices singing a sad, sweet hymn of the crucifixion awakens us at six o'clock. It is pitch dark, and the only light in the house is from the little kerosene wick, smaller than a birthday candle, burning in the hall between our room and the children's. The singing comes closer, then fades away, then gets a little louder as the girls turn to sing toward the nurses' house a hundred yards away, then fades out entirely. It is a beautiful, haunting song, and I don't recognize it. I switch on the flashlight to check the time, then we both get up. It is still dark, but dawn is just breaking when we walk down to the cemetery twenty minutes later. We push through the tall manyara hedge and stand facing the graves and the rising sun. The Christian cemetery is only about a hundred fifty by fifty feet in dimensions and there are no grave markers. We stand quietly, shivering a little in the cool morning breeze. There are about forty people here, five of them missionaries, the rest Africans. The elders of the church are here, most in European dress, others in somber black native dress. One old man wears a "kanzu," a white gown hanging straight from the neck to the ankles without belt or other adornment which looks for all the world like an old-fashioned night-

140

grown; not too many years ago this was the standard attire for the Iramba male. The older women are dressed in their bright-colored shukas, with a second cloth draped over the head and shoulders and one end thrown across in front from one shoulder to the other. All the young girls are in brightly colored European-style dresses, some with the head scarves like those worn by the older women.

Someone starts up a hymn in Kinylamba, and Alice Turnbladh holds her hymnbook up for us to see. I hope that the sermon will not be in the local dialect also. We have learned to pronounce Kinylamba, and occasionally flashes of understanding come, but for the most part it is unintelligible to us. We sing three songs, wondering who is going to hold the service, since as far as we can see there is no pastor here. As we finish the third hymn, Mr. Samweli Makala pushes through the hedge and opens his Bible. Mr. Makala is one of our medical assistants. He is neatly and conservatively dressed in dark coat and pants with white shirt and dark tie. He speaks to us for about fifteen minutes, fortunately in Swahili, telling the part of the Easter story concerned with the early morning visit of Mary Magdalene to the sepulcher. It is an oft-heard story, but standing there in the graveyard, with the sun's rays just finding their way into the desolate burial ground, one can appreciate the words of the scripture as Mr. Makala reads them, "Mnamtafuta Yesu Mnazareti, aliyesulibiwa; amefufuka, hayupo hapa. . . ." You are seeking Jesus of Nazareth, he who was crucified; he has arisen, he is not here. . . .

Certainly he isn't here; anyone can see that. Amefufuka. He has arisen. He has proceeded us from this place—he has gone out of this place of death into the places where people *live*. . . .

We walk slowly home.

Eric and Barbara are still asleep, and we wake them

gently. No sooner are they awake than they jump out of bed with little squeals of excitement, hunting spasmodically for the colored Easter eggs we had all colored the previous day and which Edna and I hid last night. The hunt comes out enough of a tie that both kids are happy.

After a breakfast of banana pancakes, we leisurely get ready for church, and at about 9:30 we start out on the ten-minute walk to church. We want to get there early, because this church is no different from our churches at home on Easter and Christmas—everyone comes. I think a great number of people in the United States have the erroneous idea that the heathen once converted to Christianity becomes a model Christian and is suddenly transformed from a dirty, ignorant, bloodthirsty savage into a clean, educated, peaceful, Christian citizen. Both the "before" and "after" pictures are, of course, erroneous—at least here in Iramba-land. It is true, as we have seen in a previous chapter, that over the years Christian missionaries have wrought these changes, but not overnight, and unfortunately, the Christian thus made has not always remained starry-eyed and true to his new beliefs. And those who have have produced second and then third generation Christians who oftentimes assume the same type of lukewarmness that is all too common in the "inherited" Christianity of the majority of Christians in the United States. This is an unpalatable morsel for many mission-minded idealists to swallow.

And it shows up on Easter Sunday when the average year-around attendance of a hundred fifty to three hundred soars to five or six hundred. This morning the church is jammed. The rough wooden benches are bulging, and since they occupy only the front two thirds of the church, the back part is packed with people seated on the floor. People also are crowded around the doors and windows.

The service lasts two hours. First is the normal form of service, following the liturgy in the hymnal, with Pastor Tomasa Musa singing the liturgy. Then Pastor Musa preaches a really inspired sermon. This is followed by the introduction of a man from another area who preaches almost another full-length sermon; this man is a member of a very strictly fundamentalist group of Christians who call themselves "Wandugu," or "Friends" (not to be confused with the Quakers)—this group works within the framework of the legitimate churches and is semi-secret in its aims. Following this second discourse, which is very unnerving to listen to because it describes in vivid detail the speaker's past sins and wickednesses from which he is now separated and saved, there are several songs by the school children from the Kiomboi African Primary School. And how these children sing! They stand stony-faced and half scared to death, but when their leader pokes his finger into the air, they let go with all the restraint of a through-train going through Midville. The church fairly vibrates.

After the songs by the children, the collection is taken up while we sing a hymn. This morning there are several reed baskets, but on more than one occasion I have seen the ushers literally pass a hat. After the collection, the announcements; and then with the final hymn we all get up and file ouside to form a circle to be dismissed with the benediction.

Except for the extra half-hour, the service is much like other services here. There is a simplicity in these services, as there is a simplicity in the church building, solid and rectangular. There is no organ or piano. There is no choir. There are no acolytes (no candles either). There are no stained-glass windows, and as a matter of fact, there are practically no windows, most of them having been broken and not replaced. At first I was favorably impressed by all this lack of the visible externals which we associate with the average American church. But, now, I am not so sure. I miss the solemn organ music which drowns out the whispers of the tongue-waggers as the congregation gathers. I miss the subdued colored light that filters through the beautifully colored figures of biblical characters in the windows (how long has it been since *you* noticed them?). I miss the coordinated symphony of the trained voices of the choir. I miss all of these "externals" which convert a meeting place into a worshiping place. Habit is a powerful force. It may be that the African in our churches remembers with nostalgia his own church at home. Certainly Wesley's churches, the frontier churches, and many other churches, including the synagogues that Christ preached in, were plain and bare and simple.

The remainder of Easter Sunday is quiet and restful, as most Sundays are. In the late afternoon we all gather at Joe Norquist's for supper, everyone participating in the roundup of food. Two of the nurses, Greta and Polly, I think, have brought back a ham from Arusha some weeks before, so we have that with deviled eggs, potatoes, sweet corn, and some kind of gooey dessert. We had planned to eat outside, but the daily thunderstorm comes about two hours late and drowns out that idea.

At 7:30 we have our usual Sunday evening devotions, which are primarily for the missionaries and are held in English. This particular Sunday Polly (Pauline Swanson) is in charge, and as luck would have it, she has come down just today with a severe attack of malaria. She does well in her presentation, but we all feel rather sorry for her. She has not been taking chloroquin because of a supposed allergy to it, and unfortunately she has not developed enough natural immunity to it. (We were later able to demonstrate that she actually was not allergic to chloroquin, for which she was very grateful.)

After devotions, we meet at one of the nurses' homes for cake and coffee and some more chitchat.

And this was our Easter. Much like home, at least as much as we could make it. There is a tendency to try to make our special holidays as similar as we can to our remembered way of life. In our daily life there is the constant effort throughout all our dealings to conform as closely as possible to the Africans' way of doing things, so that on occasion we just like to do things our way for a change, at least in our homes.

15

THE WAKINDIGA

The shadows of past events fall on the pages of our morning newspaper, blurring the print. We read of events which happened yesterday, or was it ten years ago—or a hundred? Is the nationalism of the new Africa, which has driven the English and the Belgians and the French out of East Africa and the Congo and Algeria, any different from the Serbian nationalism that killed Archduke Franz Ferdinand of Austria and touched off World War I? Can we not learn of the past, and therefore learn from the past?

All of us like to look into the past. We cannot look into the future except in imagination, in hope, and in anticipation, so we look into the past for the omens and the facts and the ideas which will shape the coming events. We also look into the past just to see what it was like "way back when" before we were born.

Most of us are content to read about the way things were. Anthropologists are not. They explore and dig away at the layered earth, piecing together the fragmented past. And once in a while, a civilization is found which does not need to be glued together—for it still exists in its original state.

The reader is about to be introduced to such a society.

146

In the letter you are now going to read, I describe a week-long visit to the tribe of people called the Wakindiga. The letter was written just a few days after I returned to Kiomboi, and it was sent to Pastor Marc Gravdahl, then the pastor of Grace Lutheran Church in Eau Claire, Wisconsin. I have wanted to include in this report something of the missionary work done in Wakindiga-land and originally I intended to write a separate chapter. But the spontaneity of the letter written with immediate memory of events stenciled into my brain and with the help of notes penciled on scraps of paper will give a truer picture than I could paint now. Since I wrote the letter, I have learned more facts about this fascinating people and possibly have developed more of an understanding of the work done among them, but I do not believe I could again recapture the awe-filled moments in Sha Kitundu's camp as well as I have in the letter.

Join me now, as we travel fifty miles from Kiomboi, over the Isanzu ridge, across the plains of Sibiti, into the mountains of Kindira, and backward in time many thousands of years.

February 10, 1963

Dear Marc,

During the past week I have had an experience which stands out even among all the interesting experiences I have been through in the past six months.

Pastor Bob Ward and I had gradually warmed a friendship out of casual meetings over the half year I had been in Africa. We visited him and his family for a weekend and he invited me to accompany him into a roadless area near his home base of Isanzu on a foot safari. Bob has

147

been working with the tribe of bushmen known as the Wakindiga periodically for years and full-time for the past year. Bob is thirty-six—had his birthday the day before we set out—and is as rugged a specimen of manhood as ever preached a sermon or toted a rifle, both of which he loves to do.

We set out by Land Rover early Monday morning, heading south off the Isanzu ridge, dropping gradually off the ridge to the east, and finally starting the long descent north into the valley of the Sibiti River. After about an hour we left the track, which itself had been difficult enough to identify, and struck off into the bush to the northeast on a track that could scarcely be seen at all! I asked Bob how he had ever found this track in the first place. "Find it?" he asked, laughing, "Bwana, we made it!" And then I realized that Bob Ward was the only white man who ever came regularly into this country. We continued downhill through grass that varied from two to ten feet tall, through baobab forests, acacia, and thornbush, for about another hour. We stopped under a big shade tree, and then taking our guns, walked about two miles further. Although Bob minimized the fact that this was lion, leopard, snake, and rhino country, I never saw him go a foot from camp without his rifle. I know that it took several hours before I could keep myself from scanning the rocks and hillsides for signs of hostile animal life!

We crossed a dry river and began climbing again, soon coming to a village built by Sumuni and his small clan.

A little background picture is needed here to fully appreciate Sumuni and his village. The Wakindiga are a small tribe numerically—about a thousand people who occupy a particularly wild area of about two hundred fifty square miles at the southwestern tip of Lake Eyasi, which you will find a hundred miles west of Arusha on most maps of Tanganyika. Anthropologists classify them as true bushmen. They build no permanent shelters preferring to erect little grass huts perhaps eight to nine feet in diameter on a scanty framework of thin branches. Then they move on every few weeks or months, following the game and searching for new unharvested roots. Their primary diet is roots (more about this later), and they will leave areas of abundant game to find an unused area of edible roots. They also collect honey from hollows in the giant baobabs which grow to a thickness of up to thirty feet, pounding pegs into the otherwise unclimbable mammoths and scooping out the honey by the handfuls, as unmindful of the bees as one can be in such a circumstance!

They plant nothing, therefore raise nothing. They also move into areas of heavy berry growth during the ripening season. There are no literate "Digas," and no written language, although practically all the men know Swahili in addition to their tribal language, Kikindiga; the women speak no Swahili. The men wear a loincloth loosely wrapped around the waist; the women wear tattered animal skins around the waist with another skin over the shoulders like a shawl for warmth when necessary. Both men and women wear brightly colored bead necklaces and bracelets. Mostly they still leave their dead in the bush, although on the edges of their country where they are coming into contact with the increasingly advancing Sukumas (who now number several million and include the cities of Tabora, Mwanza, Shinyanga, and Nzega), they are beginning to bury their dead.

They live in single family groups, with three to seven adults and about the same number of children, separated from their fellows by many miles. The reason for this is obvious: any given area can only produce so many roots, berries, and honey, and too large a clan would eat itself out of a livelihood too frequently. Theirs is a continual search for food. They are monogamous primarily for the same reason; some cultures encourage polygamy because that means more women to till more ground and consequently produce more food, but if the food is at an unchangeable maximum already, more women only means more mouths (and more children). There is no marriage ceremony as we know it, only a verbal contract between suitor and bride's father, and the bride-price is a token only—a couple of arrows, a skin, or so, rather than a really stringent price such as is asked for brides in a more affluent society.

Their language is distinctive, called a click language. I couldn't possibly describe it for you, although in rapid conversation one is reminded of Donald Duck at times.

Now back to Sumuni. We came into his camp at noon and found it nearly deserted. One young man, Maiombo, was sitting on a large boulder overlooking the village making poisoned arrows, and two women and some children sat in the shadow of a house plaiting baskets. The other three men and three women were out searching for food, and Maiombo had been left with the two women to guard them. One of the women was eight and nine-tenths months pregnant and we expected her to deliver at any moment, and the other woman had a child ill with malaria (which we were able to check in less than forty-eight hours with chloroquin). One man always stays with the women in camp because of the predatory habits of the Masai on the northern borders of the territory.

Maiombo welcomed Bob heartily and greeted me cordially. The women eyed us more or less indifferently, or at least with no obvious emotion. We accompanied Maiombo back onto his lookout and watched him make his arrows. The shafts he had already carved—about three feet long for the animal arrows, and over five feet long for the bird arrows—all as "straight as an arrow." Fletchings of kanga (wild guinea fowl) feathers were glued to the shafts. The glue is made by chewing a certain tuber. When the spittle is expectorated, it coagulates like iron. The tip is of steel, broad and flat, thin as a playing card, sharp as a razor, and is detachable by means of a three-inch shaft which fits into a hole at the end of the main arrow. The poison is laboriously made by grinding a handful of small brown seeds between two stones, occasionally adding a small fragment of a black substance which is carved from the heart of the root of a climbing vine, and then making a paste of this material by adding warm water. The paste is then applied to the entire length of the detachable head, about four inches or more, and dried in the sun, to be covered with a thin strip of wild pigskin wound around it.

I looked around the camp. There were five permanent grass houses, about ten feet high and perhaps twenty feet in diameter, with a tunnel-like entrance of grass that reminded me immediately of Eskimo igloos. We visited Sumuni's house immediately after a violent storm and the inside was dry as could be. At the far end of the house was a low frame upon which sat the huge baskets of grain. On one side was a skin or two; in the middle a fire; along other sides hoes, grinding stones, and gourds for water. You will already have noted striking differences in this camp from what I described as typical of the Wakindiga—dry, well-built houses, baskets of grain, hoes for cultivating. For Sumuni has a "shamba"—this little clan is surrounded by fields of corn, millet, tomatoes, cucumbers, papaya. Two years ago, Sumuni broke from the tribal customs of uncounted centuries and *planted a garden*. A world-shaking event? Maybe not to 180 million Americans who could plant a garden if they had to but don't have to because only one in twenty Americans need to raise food for the rest of us. Maybe not even to

Sumuni himself. But just think of the significance of this
event! No longer tied to the string that pulls others around
the hills, constantly looking for food! No longer limited to
a one-family group if he wishes to be more gregarious!
Now able to control his own food supply, maybe someday
even to raise more than he needs to eat—to be able to
sell or barter food for other necessities.

So far Sumuni does not grow enough to be totally self-
sufficient, and a crop failure could send him into the bush
again, but the seed has been planted in the mind as well
as in the ground, and God grant that it continue to grow
in both.

We set up our tents alongside the village and lived there
for five days. We got to know the men quite well—
Sumuni himself, Maiombo, Maidona, Kingu—but not the
women since they don't know the Swahili language for
one thing, and by custom don't join so readily in conversation and activities. We ate native food; in the morning
we had *uji* (a thin corn meal) and mangoes; in the evening *ugale* (a thick corn meal) and usually a bird shot
during the day. At noon we ate what was available,
peanuts one day, a bird another, ugale another, uji a
fourth. We sat with the people around their campfires at
night, in their houses during the day, and on their lookout rock by the hour, especially in the late afternoon.
I could see a pattern developing. Bob's idea is to live
with these people, eat with them, talk with them, hunt
with them, sit quietly with them, teach them, preach to
them, pray with them, love them.

One morning at dawn we set out with Sumuni,
Maiombo, and Maidona, and hunted steadily for six hours
along a dry river bed. We were looking especially for a
wild pig, but would have taken anything. We saw only a
young female greater kudu and a giraffe, both of which are
illegal game for rifles. The men all carried their bows, one

poison arrow, and four or five bird arrows with tips like a target arrow with one small barb. We saw the tracks of leopard, pig, hyena, dik-dik, and a rhino—the latter so fresh that the Africans crept along warily peering through the dense jungle vines and foliage for a glimpse of the monster. We never saw him. The natives fear the rhino; the lion will run; the leopard is extremely timid; the elephant must be provoked; but the rhino will charge unprovoked. Many hunters feel a rhino should be shot on sight, since the chances are that he will charge, and a straight-on shot is less likely to stop him than a broadside through the heart. We continued on until the noon heat and lack of food caused me to really feel the six hours' walking full tilt in the sand! Bob and the Africans were still going strong. Some uji and tea and an hour of sleep felt mighty good, and later in the afternoon we had some ugale and a kanga Bob shot while I was resting.

One afternoon we went out with Maiombo and Maidona to an area of extremely dense jungle of vines and creepers and tangled foliage. Sumuni and the women were already there digging roots. A particular vine is sought and traced through the undergrowth to its emergence from the ground. At this point an area is cleared of undergrowth over an area of perhaps twenty-five square feet, and the digging starts in earnest, first with a large hoe; then, as the tubers are neared, with a sharpened stick. More superficial to the edible roots, the diggers encountered an occasional root which they removed, smelled, and then threw away—poisonous, they said. I believed them and didn't try any! The soil is red clay, and the diggers get right down in the hole on hands and knees, unearthing each root tenderly and gingerly. The roots themselves resemble sweet potatoes in size and shape and are like pears in consistency. We helped dig a little and ate right along with the "Digas." The root is very good-tasting,

cool, juicy, and sweet. We worked in the vines all afternoon. Bob and I sat and talked with the men most of the
time, while one of them continued digging, passing the
roots out from the hole. Sometimes the digger would eat
it; sometimes someone else, and once in a while, a root
would go unscathed into a pile to be taken back and eaten
later (usually for breakfast or a midday snack). At one
time Maiombo was digging and was passing out tuber
after tuber to Maidona, who in turn was eating every one
until it became obvious to Maiombo what was happening;
and thereafter with every tuber he would ask, "Umeshiba
bado?" Are you full yet? And Maidona just kept eating
and grinning, enjoying the fruits of his friend's labor!
It was quite comical and caused much laughter among
those who could hear what was going on.

Each evening, we sat with the men, women, and children around the community campfire in the open space
within the circle of houses, talking over the days' activities. It was nearly full moon, and the skies were clear
except for one evening. Bob spent about a half hour each
evening playing records of sermons and songs in Kikindiga and showing film strips or giving short talks which
were translated from Swahili into Kikindiga by Sumuni.
After each "service," they would all say with great re-
spect and sincerity, "Songela," a Bantu word meaning
"Thank you." Sumuni and his clan are about ready for
baptism. Missionaries have been in occasional contact with
him for years, and Bob has been working with him quite
regularly for a year. Bob's whole life is with these people,
and he spends weeks at a time camping in their villages,
coming out for a few days or a week periodically. He told
me if he didn't have to go home on furlough this summer,
he could really make great progress in the next two
years.

Just a word about the composite personality of these

people, drawn from my own very short week with them and Bob's long years with them. They are a gentle people, soft-spoken but not shy or reserved. Quite the reverse. They laugh easily, like little practical jokes (typified by Maidona eating all the roots Maiombo could dig), love to sing and to dance; unfortunately I didn't see any of their dances because they only dance in total darkness, therefore only at night when there is no moon. Their aversion to murder and death itself is exaggerated to the extreme that they hate to even talk about it. They have their own code of ethics, their system of mores, their own civilization, all admittedly quite different from ours, but there nevertheless. They want no quarrel with any man. They do not quarrel among themselves, or at least they are importuned not to, and it is very bad manners to raise one's voice against another. They are not interested in learning to read or write and actually may rebel against education when it eventually reaches out to them. They are at home in the trackless forest and on the yellowing or greening veld. They are among the last people in Africa to be allowed to continue hunting with poison arrows, and no game is illegal for them.

One day we set out at dawn, along the track on which we had come to Sumuni's camp, by Land Rover down and down and down the hillside with Sumuni pointing out the way, until we came to a dry river bed we could not cross. Leaving the Land Rover, we struck out along the river, now hot in the late morning sun. Finally we came to a break in the dense growth alongside the bank, and left the river along a trail at first indiscernible to me. The trail wound slowly up the hill from the dry river bed and climbed steadily and tortuously through nearly waist-high grass to the top, about five hundred feet from the valley floor. I could feel the pull in the thigh muscles and gluteal muscles despite six months in Africa and four days on foot in the land of the Wakindiga. Cresting the ridge, we saw three grass huts perched on the summit which at first glance seemed to be deserted even as Sumuni's had seemed. We soon saw that a pitiful skeleton of a girl sat huddled beside an extinguished fire clutching a black shuka around her wasted body. Her eyes were nearly swollen shut and she opened them with a great effort and greeted us with an almost inaudible, "Shaiamu" (the sun is coming up). I could hardly take my eyes off her, she was so pitiful. My first thought was TB or malignancy, and when I had a chance to take a history and examine her later she did indeed seem to be suffering from a left renal lesion, either tuberculous or cancerous. She was obviously dying and knew it, and was resigned. I shall never forget the look in her eyes as I reached into her hut to grasp her hand in farewell as we left, later in the day.

Maiombo walked along the ridge a hundred yards or so and summoned the rest of the clan with a whistle. Within an hour or so the women and children came in with loads of firewood and edible roots. After about another hour, during which Bob and I made some tea and ate some peanuts (lunch for the day), Sha Kitundu came into camp. Not from Wakindiga lineage himself, he has taken on the ways of his adopted people and is now the leader of this little clan, and the only man. He is a big, strong, coal-black man with heavy muscles and a gleaming friendly smile. We sat and talked with him most of the afternoon about various things—hunting, food-gathering, and the rains. Bob has this clan close to baptism too, and after a short sermon which Sha Kitundu translated sentence by sentence to the women, Bob discussed with him whether or not he wanted to be baptized. Sha Kitundu talked this over at some length with the women, then quietly said, "Nakubali." I agree.

I felt the solemnity of the moment. I felt the power that flowed from God through his apostle Bob Ward into this son of God who was not yet a man of God. I had witnessed what few have been privileged to witness—the final acceptance of the Christian faith by a man born a heathen of heathen parents in a hostile land of thorn and leopard and disease. Impressive also, as I think back on it, was that this was not the emotional response of the moment, succumbing to emotions heated by inflammatory speech and the equatorial African sun. This was the calm acceptance of a faith which was brought to him by a messenger of God who had accepted the admonition to go unto all parts of the earth and preach the gospel.

How will this affect the life of Sha Kitundu and his people? Will he now desire to be educated? Will he now desire to plant a garden, or move out of the land of his fathers, or give up his customs? How will his life be different? No one can answer this. He may do all of these things; he may do none. He may only accept Christianity for a year or two; or he may so live his life that his sons themselves will become ministers of God. Bob Ward is the first to recognize that baptism is only the beginning. The Christian life and tenets of Jesus must be taught and taught and taught! One cannot quit with the baptismal service, important as it is.

Well, Marc, this was my week. Like finishing a good book, my mind flicks back through the pages of the week, reliving each day, reluctant to let it go. This is one book I would like to read again; I may not understand completely what put Bob Ward there in the first place, but I can understand what keeps him there.

Sincerely,

Birney

EPILOGUE

The rains have come. Our barrels are packed with a few of the things we brought with us and with a lot of the things we have collected in Africa to remind us of these days and these people.

These people. The tears fairly start to my eyes as I think of saying goodbye. What will I say? Goodbye, Samson Paulo, come see us sometime! Goodbye, Danieli Makala, don't take any wooden nickels! Goodbye, Eliasafi, take it easy! No, I can't say any of those things, even though this is the customary American way of breaking up the emotions which threaten to disrupt leave-takings. I can say these things to Joe and Marilyn and to Greta, Polly, Ann, and Alice, but to the Africans I can only say, "Kwa heri, Tutaonana." Goodbye, till we meet again.

The rain beats on the metal roof with a throbbing in its voice. The thunder rolls across the sea of bush and thorn outside my window and my neighbor's cows scamper for the security of their boma. Across on the other side of the compound, in the hospital, the patients' relatives crowd the entry ways and sit straight-legged in the aisles between the beds. In the primary school, the teacher raises his voice to make himself heard above the racket on the roof.

And on this eve of my departure, I raise my voice above

the storm and cry out in frustration. I cry out for the
Christians of Iramba-land who have heard the voice of
God speaking to them, and have accepted the gospels of
Jesus Christ, and have built a building for his worship,
and sing praises to his name—but who will not accept
the stewardship of his gifts to them. I cry out for the
missionaries of Iramba-land who have come to bring the
ministries of preaching, and teaching, and healing to the
heathen and ignorant and sick—but who in order to keep
going must oftentimes remind themselves that they have
come to love, not to be loved. I cry out for the politicians
who have sent the British home, and have seated themselves in the chairs of authority, and have said to the
world, "we are ready to govern ourselves"—but who too
often forget that with the privileges of self-rule come the
responsibilities to the people. And I cry out for the school-
boys and girls who have grasped at education like drown-
ing men in a raft, and have learned that 2 x 2 is four,
and can tell you about Julius Nyerere and George Wash-
ington—but who also are learning that nationalism is a
god who demands loyalty with jealous impatience.

The sounds of the house are drowned out by the
deafening roar on the roof. A steady drip of water starts
to fall on the corner of my desk. There is a towel there
already, in anticipation.

Earlier this afternoon, with the coolness of the rains
already on the wind, anticipation of that drip was easy,
even with my limited meteorological knowledge. Anticipation of the Iramba-land of the future is, however, difficult, and the place of Kiomboi Hospital even more so.
Iramba-land will change. Already half the children are
in school who should be in school. Already the churches
are going through the throes of Africanization, with missionaries in the pulpits dwindling in number as their
black opposite numbers take over. Already there is un-

rest in the labor unions and the once-sufficient minimum wage laws are scaling upward. Already the animal skins once worn have given way to cloth wrap-arounds, and many people are dressed in shirt and tie. Already the men know Swahili, the *lingua franca* of East Africa, and more and more women are learning the language of their country.

Tracks into the bush will become roads, and dry-weather roads will become all-weather roads, and the seventy miles of blacktop reaching south from Arusha will become a hundred, and someday will reach Singida, and then Kiomboi. Trucks now owned by the Indians and the missions will find their way into private and co-operative African ownership. Someday there will be a telephone line to the Kiomboi Lutheran Hospital.

When these things happen, the Lutheran Hospital will still be here. The doctor-in-charge will be an African, graduate of the Kilimanjaro Christian Medical Center at Moshi, and people will recall that Dr. Bob Jensen spent the spring and summer years of his life in seeing this dream come true. By that time, it will be ancient history that Pastor Lud Melander first brought modern medicines to Iramba-land in the form of aspirin for pain, quinine for fever, and potassium permanganate for sores. It will scarcely be remembered, however, that in the next thirty years a long list of diseases virtually disappeared from Iramba-land—sleeping sickness, smallpox, yaws, tropical ulcers, elephantiasis, beriberi, and the plague.

The Kiomboi Lutheran Hospital was the center of this medical drama and will continue to be so. It cannot be otherwise. It must reach outward from itself to the plains of Kidaru, to the valley of the Barabaig, into the mountains of Kindira, there to stand and say, "I must work the works of him that sent me, while it is day: the night cometh when no man can work" (John 9:4, KJV).

160